Twayne's English Authors Series

Sylvia E. Bowman, *Editor*

INDIANA UNIVERSITY

Thomas Henry Huxley

TEAS 84

Thomas Henry Huxley

By ALBERT ASHFORTH

Brooklyn College

Twayne Publishers, Inc.   : :   New York

Preface

The struggle to win acceptance for the ideas contained in the *Origin of Species* is one of the most dramatic and exciting stories in the history of English culture. The initial impact of Darwin's epoch-making volume was principally scientific, and the immediate result of its publication was that a few scientists strongly favored it and a great many just as strongly opposed it. Hardly any remained uncommitted for very long. The handful of men who stood by Darwin during the first difficult years after the book's publication did so at great risk to their reputations, and this fact partly accounts for the ferocity of the warfare they conducted in an effort to secure a fair hearing for the book. Of this group none emerged from the smoke of the now legendary controversy as a more dashing and inspiring figure than young scientist Thomas Henry Huxley.

"It is doubtful," Huxley later wrote of the *Origin*, "if any single book, except the *Principia*, ever worked so great a revolution in science, or made so deep an impression on the general mind."[1] It is safe to say that the revolution would not have come about nearly so rapidly if Huxley had not given his all-out support to Darwin. The revolution would have occurred, to be sure; but it would have taken longer. Huxley's incredibly effective campaign to win a fair hearing for evolution—and for which he earned the soubriquet "Darwin's Bulldog"—represents the aspect of his career for which he today is best remembered. But Huxley actually occupied himself with the defense of Darwin for only a decade—between 1860 and 1870. After that he turned his attention to other matters. Capitalizing on notoriety acquired during the evolution controversy, he produced a steady stream of articles, books, and essays in which he subjected nearly every facet of English civilization and culture to scrutiny and criticism. In so doing, he became one of the most influential men of his generation.

It is this aspect of Huxley's career with which this book is primarily concerned, for it was during the years after 1870 that he did most of the writing for which he is remembered. What Huxley was trying to do was to analyze and explain the impact the new findings of science were having upon the traditional values and assumptions which underlie Western culture—more specifically, upon education, theology, philosophy, politics, morality, and art. I have brought together his writings in such a way as to, I hope, make this pattern clear. These questions—the significance of which is all too plain today—concerned only a handful of men in Huxley's time; for, if anything, the "two cultures"—the sciences and the humanities—were even farther apart in the nineteenth century than they are now. If one compiles a list of the ten most influential essayists in the last century, one sees that John Stuart Mill, Matthew Arnold, Walter Pater, John Ruskin, and Cardinal Newman all missed the consequences that were to follow from the rise of science in their time. The contemporaries of Huxley who were closest to him in this respect were John Tyndall, Herbert Spencer, and, to a limited extent, Walter Bagehot.

But not even they understood the drift of the times quite as well as Huxley, nor could they think so clearly on such a wide variety of subjects, and certainly none of them wrote so well. Why we tend to remember him more as a thinker and writer than as a scientist has been explained by his grandson, Aldous Huxley: "As a scientific man, Huxley, like all his great contemporaries and predecessors, is now a mere historical figure.... As a literary man, however, he is still a living force. His non-technical writings have the persistent contemporariness that is the quality of all good art."[2]

What gives Huxley added importance is the fact that he was, quite frankly, a spokesman for the scientific viewpoint. Huxley, it should be remembered, was educated as a physician; he made his living as a teacher of science; he lived and worked in a milieu inhabited mostly by scientists; and he honestly considered science as a calling to be superior to all others. Yet, and here is his distinguishing characteristic, his culture was so broad that he was no less at home in the humanities. He was a unique figure among the great essayists of the nineteenth century.

How Huxley became the man he was is a fascinating story.

Preface

The beginning chapters deal with this aspect of Huxley's career: his cruise on the *Rattlesnake*, one of the great scientific voyages of the last century; his literary apprenticeship, served as a writer of scientific articles; his initial disdain for evolutionary theory and his subsequent "conversion"; his defiance of Bishop Wilberforce at Oxford, which brought him national prominence, but which just as easily could have consigned him to lasting oblivion; and finally, the activities which brought him fame as "Darwin's Bulldog."

Lastly, I have tried to analyze Huxley's achievement from the standpoint of our science-steeped twentieth century. There is no question that Huxley addressed himself to subjects that have great pertinence today and that he expressed himself in terms that have not often been bettered. However, in the years since his death, Huxley has chiefly been admired by scientists but overlooked by students of the humanities. This fact is unfortunate since Huxley's point of view can go a long way in helping us to understand the relationship between what have come to be known as the "two cultures." Huxley did not produce a systematized and comprehensive body of writing aimed at explaining this relationship; but, as one becomes familiar with what he had to say, his point of view becomes marvelously clear. Even while one may disagree with him, object to what may appear to be inadequate or biased explanations, or on occasion protest against seeming contradictions, there is nevertheless a consistent view of the totality of natural phenomena to be discerned in Huxley's writing—and this view is no less informed by the vision of a man of letters than by that of a man of science.

Many friends and colleagues have given invaluable aid and advice during the writing of this book. Mr. Francis E. Haney was the source of a number of key suggestions, as was Professor J. Vernon Jensen of the University of Minnesota. Members of the library staff of the Imperial College of Science and Technology helped immeasurably while I was reading Huxley's papers at the College. Particularly invaluable assistance was rendered by Mrs. Jeanne Pingree, chief archivist, and Mrs. Yvonne Cormeau. I would also like to thank the Trustees of the College for permitting me to read and quote from the Huxley Collection.

ALBERT ASHFORTH
Brooklyn College

Contents

Contents

Chronology

1825   Thomas Huxley born, May 4, at Ealing, Middlesex, near London.

1833–   Attended Ealing School.
1835

1835   Family moved to Coventry; began program of self-education.

1841   Began study of medicine.

1842   Matriculated at London University.

1845   Bachelor of Medicine, London University.

1846–   Voyage on H.M.S. *Rattlesnake*.
1850

1850   Granted leave for research by the navy.

1851   Elected Fellow of the Royal Society.

1852   Awarded Royal Society Gold Medal.

1854   Resigned from the navy; appointed lecturer in Natural History at the Royal School of Mines in London.

1855   Married Henrietta Anne Heathorn; received appointment as naturalist to the Geological Survey.

1856   Traveled with John Tyndall to Switzerland.

1858   Delivered Croomian Lecture "On the Theory of the Vertebrate Skull"; beginning of the controversy with Sir Richard Owen.

1859   Reviewed the *Origin of Species* in the London *Times*.

1860   Defended Darwin at the meeting of the British Association at Oxford.

1863   *Man's Place in Nature*.

1864   x Club formed; "Criticisms on the Origin of Species."

1868   "On the Physical Basis of Life"; "On a Piece of Chalk"; "A Liberal Education."

1869   Metaphysical Society formed; engaged in controversy with English Comteists.

1870 Elected to the First London School Board; *Lay Sermons, Addresses, and Reviews.*

1871 Elected Secretary of the Royal Society; "Mr. Darwin's Critics"; "Administrative Nihilism."

1872 Traveled to Egypt and Italy for reasons of health; elected Lord Rector of Aberdeen University.

1873 *Critiques and Addresses.*

1876 Visited America.

1877 *Physiography.*

1879 *Hume;* began studying Greek.

1880 "Science and Culture"; beginning of controversy with Matthew Arnold.

1883 Elected President of the Royal Society.

1884 Traveled to Italy.

1885 Retired from the School of Mines; first controversy with William Gladstone.

1887 Controversy with the Duke of Argyll.

1888 Awarded the Copley Medal of the Royal Society.

1889 Agnosticism controversy.

1892 Renewed controversy with Gladstone; *Essays On Some Controverted Questions;* elected to the Privy Council.

1893 Delivered Romanes Lecture at Oxford, "Evolution and Ethics"; *Collected Essays,* volumes I–IV.

1894 *Collected Essays,* volumes V–IX; participated in British Association meeting at Oxford.

1895 Died June 29.

CHAPTER 1

A Young Scientist

THE professional career of Thomas Henry Huxley began, as did that of Charles Darwin, with a sea voyage. Huxley was twenty-one years of age and seven months past graduation from London's Charing Cross Hospital when the "donkey frigate" H.M.S. *Rattlesnake,* under the command of Captain Owen Stanley, weighed anchor on December 3, 1846; it was bound for the waters of Australia and New Guinea and for one of the most memorable scientific voyages of the century.

Mere chance had induced Huxley, who was sailing as assistant surgeon, to apply for a naval commission. Indeed, it is somewhat startling to learn how great a part chance actually played in Huxley's early life. His original ambition had been to become an engineer; but, when his two older sisters married physicians, their influence seems to have had a considerable effect in determining the subsequent course of his career. When, in 1842, he won a scholarship to study medicine at Charing Cross, there could no longer be any doubt that he was fated to become a doctor. Huxley did well in his medical studies—winning at graduation a gold medal in anatomy and physiology—but he never exhibited any great interest in medicine as a calling, and, except for the time spent on the *Rattlesnake,* he never practiced. "I am not sure," he wrote in "Autobiography" (1890), "that I have not all along been a sort of mechanical engineer *in partibus infidelium.* I am now occasionally horrified to think how little I ever knew or cared about medicine as the art of healing."[1]

I Surgeon at Sea

The *Rattlesnake,* a converted twenty-eight-gun frigate, was under orders to bring back to England a full account of the geology, geography, and natural history of the waters northeast of Australia, inshore from the Great Barrier Reef, and to chart a passage through the Torres Strait of India. Such was the Admiralty's indifference to science that the ship selected for this complicated and hazardous voyage was an antiquated, wooden sailing vessel alive with cockroaches, and as Huxley described it, among "the slowest, clumsiest, and in every respect the most inconvenient ships which wear the pennant."[2] Moreover, on leaving Portsmouth the *Rattlesnake* was "in such a disgraceful state of unfitness, that her lower deck was continually under water during the voyage."[3]

Despite the sorry condition of the vessel, Huxley was nevertheless overjoyed by the assignment. The *Naval Manual* promised "encouragement and assistance to such of their officers as distinguish themselves in scientific pursuits," and Huxley regarded the voyage as a capital opportunity: he would simultaneously be able to further his career; extend his knowledge of zoology and ethnology; and, since the invertebrate sea life that inhabited tropical waters was still something of a mystery to scientific men, perhaps even advance the knowledge of British science itself. The scientific equipment of the *Rattlesnake,* however, was also haphazard. The ship had no library, and Huxley's efforts to have the Admiralty provide one proved fruitless. He brought along a number of books of his own—among them Carlyle's *Miscellanies* and *Sartor Resartus,* John Stuart Mill's *Logic,* and Dante's *Divina Commedia*—which, since he had no room in his own cabin, he was permitted to store in the chart room. He gathered his specimens with a converted meat cover of his own devising, and the conditions under which he conducted his dissections of the captured sea creatures were equally primitive.

Besides offering him an opportunity for original research, the cruise on the *Rattlesnake* gave Huxley occasion for a debut into colonial society; and during the *Rattlesnake*'s first visit to Sydney he met Henrietta Anne Heathorn, the daughter of a prosperous Sydney merchant and the woman who eventually became his wife. Since the *Rattlesnake* made Sydney a regular port of call over the course of the next four years, he and Miss Heathorn, during these breaks in his routine, began attending balls and parties with surprising frequency.

"What think you of your grave, scientific brother turning out a ball-goer and doing the 'light fantastic' to a great extent?"[4] Huxley asked his sister in a letter written in March, 1848. The news was probably received at home with surprise. Beyond the fact that Huxley's early life was studious and withdrawn, little is known of it. He was the seventh of eight children born to George Huxley. Beatrice Webb, who met him in later life (and has left a penetrating evaluation of his character), said his childhood was "supremely sad";[5] and, since Huxley himself seldom commented on his childhood in later years, most biographers and commentators have tended to accept this estimate.

Although his father was an assistant master at a semi-public school, Huxley's own schooling seems to have been almost entirely neglected. Between eight and ten, he had two years of a "pandemonium of a school," which he was just as glad to leave when, his father having lost his post, the family moved to Coventry. The boy began at this time a program of reading, but his busy parents seem to have been unaware of his precocious activities. His father possessed a good-sized library, and Huxley discovered at a tender age such writers as Carlyle and William Hamilton. At the age of twelve he was reading himself to sleep with William Hutton's *Theory of the Earth*. Huxley's study of the Italian language and of Dante dates from his fifteenth year; and, at about the same time, he studied German (the influence of Carlyle) and French. In 1842 he began his medical apprenticeship. The following year he startled everybody by winning the scholarship to Charing Cross.

II *Scientific Work on the* Rattlesnake

Huxley's scientific work on the cruise consisted chiefly of investigating the structural organization of coelenterates and mollusks. He filled countless notebooks with the results of these investigations, and subsequently he composed a number of scientific papers which he sent back to a friend, Professor Edward Forbes, at the time Professor of Geology at the Royal School of Mines in London, with the request that he investigate the possibility of publication in scientific journals. Huxley, all told, sent three papers back to England from the *Rattlesnake;* and, although he did not learn of their disposition until his return to England in 1850, all were published. The most significant was "On the Anatomy and Affinities of the Family of the Medusae," which appeared in the *Philosophic Transactions of the Royal Society for 1849.*

Through this early paper of Huxley's, English science first became aware that the Medusa, a kind of jellyfish, is composed of two layers of membrane enclosed in a stomach cavity. In the paper Huxley compared the foundation membranes of the Medusa with the serous and mucous membranes of vertebrates during early stages of development. Because the developing vertebrates exhibit foundation membranes similar to those of the Medusa, Huxley reasoned that the vertebrates had developed from the lower organisms. Huxley's paper confirmed Karl Ernst von Baer's Law concerning resemblances among backboned animals at various stages of development with invertebrated animals; Huxley's discovery later led Ernst Haeckel, the German biologist, to his Gastrea Theory, an explanation of the development of higher animals from simple multicellular organisms. Five years before, in 1844, he had made his first modest bid for scientific immortality by discovering and reporting the existence of "Huxley's Layer," an inner membrane in the root of the human hair. Thus by 1849 his competence as a scientist was already firmly established.

The effect Huxley's voyage exercised on his life was hardly less than the impression that the *Beagle* voyage made on Darwin. Not only did it shape the broad course of Huxley's later life, it had a profound effect on his personality and outlook. "It was good for me to live under sharp discipline," he subsequently wrote in 1890, "to be down on the realities of existence by living on bare necessaries ... and, more especially, to learn to work for the sake of what I got for myself out of it, even if it all went to the bottom and I along with it."[6] Such knowledge is generally dearly bought; and, while—then as now—it was the custom for men of science to serve part of their apprenticeship in the field, the early lives of men of letters are too often restricted to libraries and classrooms. By the time the voyage of the *Rattlesnake* came to an end, at Chatham, England, on November 9,

1850, the ship's assistant surgeon was not only a keen-eyed ethnologist and zoologist, but a man who had a deep acquaintance with the world and its ways.

III *London Again*

As a direct result of his paper describing the Medusa and another on "The Animal of Trigonia," which was the first time this particular type of mollusk had been observed and described by an English scientist, the young physician was known—if not by face, at least by name—to many of the most distinguished members of England's ruling scientific fraternity, and it was not long before he was rubbing shoulders with them at the meetings of various scientific societies. Edward Forbes, who had overseen the publication of his *Rattlesnake* papers and who was later to prove instrumental in securing him his first teaching post, recognized his ability and supplied the impetus for his election to the Royal Society.

Huxley's physical appearance was impressive, combining a determined expression with sparkling black eyes which could not altogether conceal a pixie sense of humor. He was tall—standing just under six feet—with a swarthy complexion, straight black hair, a high forehead, and a prominent nose, which he was in the habit of referring to as the "beak." His manner was self-confident, his speech articulate, and he generally impressed even those with whom he came in casual contact.

Two contemporaries whose acquaintance he made in 1851 after his return to London were Darwin and Herbert Spencer, and with both he struck up friendships that lasted a lifetime. Two other important associations made at the meeting of the British Association at Ipswich the following year were with Sir Joseph Hooker, the botanist, and John Tyndall, the physicist. In later years Tyndall was to become no less an eloquent spokesman for naturalism than Huxley and to achieve a position in the physical sciences comparable to that enjoyed by Huxley in the life sciences. The careers of both Hooker and Tyndall remained closely intertwined with his own. After four years of seagoing solitude, relieved only by the layovers at Sydney, the fellowship of such men was heady tonic indeed. "I have at last tasted what it is to mingle with my fellows—to take my place in that society for which nature has fitted me," he writes to Miss Heathorn in November, 1851; "and whether the draught has been a poison which has heated my veins or true nectar from the gods, lifegiving, I know not, but I can no longer rest where I once could have rested."[7] Subsequent events were to prove the "nectar" to be lifegiving.

As strange and ironic as it may now seem, Huxley, voted to the Royal Society at the tender age of twenty-six, awarded the Society's Gold Medal at twenty-seven, and recognized without qualification as the brightest star in the galaxy of England's young natural scientists, was finding it difficult to support himself. His uneasiness in this respect was aggravated, not unnaturally, by his engagement to Miss Heathorn, still living in Sydney. But science in mid-nineteenth-century England offered few paying positions; and attempts to secure teaching posts at universities in Toronto, Sydney, Aberdeen, Cork, and London were uniformly unsuccessful.

The bulk of his income at this time came from translation, reviews of scientific books, and a small salary from the Royal Navy. Immediately after landing in 1850, Huxley had applied for a leave of absence from the service, which he utilized for the purpose of arranging and putting into publishable form the material he had gathered during the cruise. However, after granting him three extensions, the navy confronted by a crisis in the Crimea, ordered him to report for duty on the H.M.S. *Illustrious.* Nothing, however, was to be allowed to stand between Huxley and his first love, science, not even a war. There followed a series of sharply worded notes between the young scientist and the Admiralty. Finally, in March 1854, after repeating for the third time his intention not to report, his name was stricken from the navy list. Huxley's career as a sailor was officially ended, and his small income was reduced.

Just two months later Professor Forbes was called to teach natural history at Edinburgh, and he suggested that his place at the School of Mines be filled by Huxley. This "temporary position" was held by Huxley until ill health forced his retirement thirty years later. He was soon able to supplement the income from his lectures through a number of other positions, notably one with a Geological Survey then investigating the English coast. As a result of his increased income, he and Miss Heathorn were married in All Saints Church on July 21, 1855. Letters of congratulation came from many of England's leading scientific figures. John Tyndall, writing from Paris, expressed the wish that Huxley's marriage would "be productive of all the felicity which your warmest friends or your own rebellious heart can desire." And a letter from Darwin contained the hope that "your marriage will not make you idle. Happiness, I fear, is not good for work."[8] Huxley may have taken Darwin's warning to heart, for Mrs. Huxley recalled some years later that, during their honeymoon at Tenby, Huxley spent much of his time dissecting fish while dictating descriptions of his work to his bride.

Like many medical men, Huxley was a notorious hypochondriac; and the "blue devils" which first possessed him after witnessing a medical dissection at the age of thirteen or fourteen regularly returned to hound him throughout his life. Nor were things made much better by Mrs. Huxley's physical condition. Shortly before their wedding Huxley had taken his prospective bride to a London physician, and he had been confidentially informed that Miss Heathorn had no more than six months to live. "Well, six months or not," Huxley told the specialist, "she is going to be my wife."[9] But, with the passage of time, Mrs. Huxley's condition showed steady improvement, and she not only survived her husband by nineteen years but became the mother of seven children. Domestic concerns and his heavy schedule were, therefore, a drain on Huxley's energies during the first years of his marriage. Darwin's fears were never realized, but according to Leonard Huxley, his father "would go down to a lecture feeling utterly unable to deliver it, and, once started, would carry it through successfully—at what cost of nervous energy was known only to those at home."[10]

By and large, however, in spite of hypochondria, attacks of toothache, and other assorted minor ailments, these were busy, happy years. Huxley's original salary at the School of Mines had been two hundred pounds but in 1855 the authorities saw fit to raise it to six hundred a year. This, in addition to twelve guineas per month from *The Westminster Review* for writing reports on contemporary scientific publications, provided him with enough to meet the needs of his growing family, and to pay the rent for a small house at 14 Waverley Place, a quiet cul-de-sac leading out of Grove End Road. The Huxleys' first child, Noel, was born on December 31, 1856; a daughter, Jessie, in 1858; another daughter, Marian, the following year; and his son Leonard in 1860.[11] Huxley's other children were Rachel, Henrietta, and Henry. As Huxley sat in the study of his little house on Waverley Place awaiting the birth of his first son, he made the following revealing and prophetic entry in his diary:

December 31, 1856. . . . 1856–7–8 must still be "Lehrejahre" to complete training in principles of histology, morphology, physiology, zoology. . . .

In 1860 I may fairly look forward to fifteen or twenty years of "Meisterjahre," and with the comprehensive views my training will have given me, I think it will be possible in that time to give a new and healthier direction to all Biological Science.

To smite all humbugs, however big; to give a nobler tone to science; to set an example of abstinence from petty personal controversies, and of toleration for everything but lying; to be indifferent as to whether the work is recognized as mine or not, so long as it is done: are these my aims? 1860 will show.[12]

Most of his energy was channeled into his lectures at the School of Mines, but his other posts included Naturalist to the Geological Survey; Curator of the Paleontological Collections; Examiner at the University of London; and he was elected in January, 1859, Secretary of the Geological Society.[13] The significance of this last post is that it marked his entrance into administrative work, a form of activity at which he eventually became wonderfully adept and which eventually led to his being named President of the Royal Society in 1883. Of course, he was also acquiring an expert's knowledge of a variety of sciences— paleontology, geology, and biology principally. Although he occasionally reviewed books and wrote other articles for various periodicals, most of Huxley's writing during these years was for scientific journals, in which he recorded the results of his original research, which was chiefly in taxonomic biology. Not until after the publication of the *Origin of Species* did he begin addressing himself in earnest to a popular audience.

IV *Early Writing*

When Huxley was married at age thirty, his fame, as well as his future hopes, rested on his scientific ability. His career at this point offers no evidence that he would one day become a force in the world of ideas and letters. No narrow specialist, he was widely read in literature and philosophy; but science was his calling, and the better part of his energies went into his lectures and laboratory work. The productions of his pen were limited to letters, scientific articles, and some lectures on scientific subjects.

A major shaping force in Huxley's literary development was the unique literary apprenticeship which he served as a writer of scientific articles. Since the subjects of many of the contributions on zoology were complex sea creatures, many of them unfamiliar even to his scientific brethren, Huxley often had to coin word descriptions which would clarify what he was writing about. The reader who leafs through the *Scientific Memoirs* will come across, in the writings done before Huxley was thirty, countless descriptions of involved physical phenomena which are extraordinary for their precision and clarity. It might be argued that the necessity to put into words a picture of these often preposterous sea denizens was the best kind of literary training Huxley might have had and that it was largely responsible for providing him with the foundation for the plain style which later became almost a personal trademark.

The following passage—taken from a paper on a kind of Rotifera, which he read before a scientific society in 1851—is not reproduced for its content, but because it represents the kind of writing that occupied Huxley almost exclusively for the decade after returning to England and because it exhibits his ability to describe with precision a complicated physical organism:

As I have seen it, the armature of the pharyngeal bulb in this species is composed of four separate pieces. Two of these are elongated triangular prisms, applied together by their flat inner faces; the upper faces are rather concave, while the outer faces are convex, and upon these the other two pieces are articulated. These last are elongated—concave internally, convex externally—and present two clear spaces in their exterior; from their inner surface, a thin curved plate projects inwards. At its interior extremity this plate is brownish and divided into five or six hard teeth, with slightly enlarged extremities.[14]

Perhaps Huxley's most striking and influential piece of work during his twenties was "The Cell Theory." This scientific article, which appeared in the *British and Foreign Medical Review* in 1853, concerns itself with the nature of life, which, by the way, was also to be the subject of one of his most controversial lectures—"On the Physical Basis of Life" (1868). The subject, of course, had fascinated scientists and philosophers from the time of Aristotle; but in the 1860's little was known of the relationship between individual cells and the whole organism. In this article Huxley showed himself to be more fully aware of the part actually played by the cell than most biologists. Single cells, Huxley says, are less the cause of organization than the result. His observation—expressed in the metaphor, cells are to the tide of life what the line of shells and weeds at the sea shore are to the living sea—was widely quoted; and it caused British biologists to re-evaluate their thinking on the subject.

A lecture delivered at St. Martin's Hall, London, in July, 1854, "On the Educational Value of the Natural History Sciences,"[15] lacks the polish which distinguishes the best of Huxley's later essays. Its imperfections may be at least partially attributed to the fact that it was composed during Huxley's first year of teaching and was delivered shortly before he joined the Geological Survey at Tenby. William Irvine has observed that Huxley, as a writer, was still heavily in the debt of Carlyle.[16] Additional significance attaches to it because, as Huxley himself in 1894 remarked, much of what he had to say later in life was "merely a development of the propositions enunciated, in this early ... piece of work."

Science, for all the practical benefits it has bestowed upon mankind, has never been without its detractors. Critics today are chiefly worried about the development of weapons capable of blowing up the world. A century ago, however, opposition came from another quarter—generally from those who were ignorant of science and its methods and who regarded scientists as a group only one step removed from alchemists and magicians.

In this lecture Huxley defines science as "nothing but *trained and organized common sense";* the great discoveries of Harvey, Claude Bernard, and Sir Charles Bell were made through experiment, deduction, and verification. Generalizations are to be made only on the basis of adequate evidence, and a priori reasoning should be avoided wherever possible. Huxley concludes by taking up the mantle of a stoic philosopher: "I cannot but think that he who finds a certain proportion of pain or evil inseparably woven up in the life of the very worms, will bear his own share with more courage and submission; and will, at any rate, view with suspicion those weakly amiable theories of the Divine government which would have us believe pain to be an oversight and a mistake—to be corrected by and by." Study of the natural sciences, he does not hesitate to add, can gratify man's moral sense as well as his intellect.

V *Huxley and Evolution*

Huxley's efforts to bring the ideas of Darwin to a large public, which resulted in his being awarded the soubriquet "Darwin's Bulldog," have already become legend and represent the work for which he is best remembered. Before the publication of the *Origin,* however, Huxley was not an evolutionist. Indeed, his ideas on the species question were quite orthodox and varied hardly at all from those held by most English scientists of the period. In the popular lectures delivered in London on such subjects as the common plans of animal forms, development, and the persistence of certain animal groups—as well as in his numerous scientific articles—he often, either overtly or implicitly, reveals himself to be opposed to evolutionary theory. He subscribed, at least during the early years of the decade, to ideas similar to those held by Sir Richard Owen, England's leading anatomist; and, probably because of Owen's authority, he accepted the archetypal theory as enunciated by Cuvier and von Baer.

At times Huxley even speaks favorably of the doctrine of Final Causes, a most un-Darwinian explanation of creation advanced by William Paley in his influential *Natural Theology;* and here and there Huxley implies that different species were, of necessity, independently created. In a contribution to the *Life and Letters of Charles Darwin* Huxley recalls his first meeting

[23]

with the author of the *Origin of Species:* "I remember ... expressing my belief in the sharpness of the lines of demarcation between natural groups and in the closeness of transitional forms with all the confidence of youth and imperfect knowledge. I was not aware, at that time, that he had then been many years brooding over the species question; and the humorous smile which accompanied his gentle answer ... long puzzled me."[17]

Despite Huxley's views, the evolutionary theory was in the air. Quite early in the decade Herbert Spencer, who never permitted lack of evidence to prevent his making a generalization, and with whom Huxley was on intimate terms, announced himself a convert. In the article "The Development Hypothesis," in the *Leader* in 1852, Spencer had ingeniously compared organic evolution with the development of a complex living organism from an egg. "The infant," he wrote, "is so complex in structure that a cyclopedia is needed to describe its constituent parts. The germinal vesicle is so simple that it may be defined in a line."[18] If the development of the child from an egg was possible, why not development of a mammal from a protozoon?

Evolutionary doctrine can, in fact, be traced back to Greece. Perhaps the first evolutionist was Anaximander (611–547 B.C.), who advanced the idea that men are descended from fish. Other Greeks—Anaximenes, Parmenides, Democritus, and Anaxagoras —also held evolutionary ideas but believed that life had originated in primordial slime. With the decline of Greece and the rise of Christianity, however, evolutionary doctrine gave way to belief in special creation; and for nearly two thousand years the Book of Genesis was regarded as giving a literal account of the origin of life. Evolutionary ideas, to be sure, popped up frequently in the works of a variety of authors, including Saint-Hilaire, Abraham Werner, and Goethe, to name a few.

But it was Darwin's own grandfather, Erasmus Darwin (1731–1802), who gave the modern world the first comprehensive account of organic evolution, when he made it the subject of section thirty-nine of his great dissertation on animal life: *Zoonomia, or the Laws of Organic Life.* The theory advanced by Erasmus Darwin is surprisingly similar in its broad outlines to the evolutionary ideas of Darwin himself, but it remained only a highly speculative theory until 1859. Charles Darwin's contribution rested not only on the massive evidence he had amassed to show that new species have arisen from common ancestral forms but also on the explanation of how evolution occurs.

In between Erasmus and Charles Darwin the chief scientific advocate of evolution had been the French naturalist Jean-Baptiste de Lamarck, who believed that acquired characteristics could be inherited and who experimented copiously, although unsuccessfully, in an effort to prove his point. Huxley was familiar with the work of Lamarck, and perhaps the French scientist's inability to discover the "hows" and "whys" may have unduly prejudiced him against evolutionary theory. But Huxley, like Darwin, came to have a high regard for Lamarck; and he may have recognized himself as the "tyro" when he wrote in reference to Lamarck that it was "the established practice for every tyro to raise his heel against the carcass of the dead lion. But it is rarely either wise or instructive to treat even the errors of a really great man with mere ridicule, and in the present case the logical form of the doctrine stands on a very different footing from its substance." At all events, Lamarck, largely because of his rivalry with Cuvier and his inability to ascertain a cause for his theory, had been shabbily treated by posterity. Huxley was among the first to perceive his stature and to offer him the recognition that he generally enjoys today.

And as Huxley's regard for Lamarck as a scientific authority increased, his regard for Sir Richard Owen diminished. Huxley's earliest references to evolutionary theory were uniformly harsh but in time began to soften. And, although no other scientist, except Charles Lyell,[19] the geologist, knew exactly the nature of the work being prepared by Darwin, there were rumors that a thunderbolt would one day be dropped into the confusion centering around the question of species. By 1859 Huxley's opinion had so changed that he was able to declare himself (as he later said) "agnostic" on the subject—by which he meant he reserved judgment on the question.

In 1844 a book had been published in England with the ungainly title *The Natural History of the Vestiges of Creation*. Its author, a Scottish publisher and journalist named Robert Chambers, had wisely decided to remain anonymous. *The Vestiges*, which argued the cause of evolution—although not very scientif-

ically—was decried uniformly by clergymen, scientists, and laymen; but, despite the universal outcry—or perhaps because of it
—it became a runaway best seller and had a tremendous influence. Owen, Herbert Spencer, and Darwin mentioned it favorably; but perhaps its greatest service was to bring the question
of organic evolution from behind the door into the room. The
topic was discussed incessantly, and the book was the object of
the memorable burlesque contained in Disraeli's *Tancred:* "You
know, all is development. The principle is perpetually going
on. First, there was nothing, then there was something; then—
I forget the next—I think there were shells, then fishes; then we
came—let me see—did we come next?"[20]

In 1854, the editor of the *British and Foreign Medical Review,* looking around for someone to review the tenth edition of
The Vestiges and remembering Huxley's contributions on "The
Cell Theory" the previous year, asked him to write it. The significance of Huxley's article lies in the fact that it clearly reflects
his firm conviction that evolutionary theory could answer no
questions respecting the origins of animal life. In a long career
as a controversialist, during which there were very few punches
pulled or sharp remarks blunted, this piece was the only work
Huxley ever came to regret for its "savagery." In this review
Huxley brought out rhetorical artillery of a kind that he did not
again employ until his controversies three decades later with
Principal Wace and Prime Minister Gladstone.

The young scientist, besides deploring the unscientific cast of
"The Vestigiarian's" mind and his speculative conclusions
("a notorious work of fiction"), expresses the wish that such "a
mass of pretentious nonsense" might better have sunk into its
proper limbo.[21] If evolution is truly a fact, Huxley asks, why
has there not been universal advance? It is a fact of paleontology
that animals and plants existed in remote geological epochs almost exactly like certain species extant today. Perhaps the most
incongruous aspect of this review, however, is its length: a dozen
closely printed pages is a great deal of space for a scientist to devote to a work of no scientific value.

Huxley was still a long way from a Darwinian view of species when, in 1856, he delivered a lecture "On Natural History
as Knowledge, Discipline and Power"[22] at the Royal Institution.

In this instance his eagerness to match the symmetry—the "Divine Geometry"—which is so readily perceived in the universe by physicists, chemists, and mathematicians with an equal beauty in the province of the naturalist, leads him to a notoriously un-Darwinian paean to the natural world. Instead of picturing it as an arena of struggle and sordid competition with no quarter given or gained, as he was later to do so often, he described the world not as a place where utility is the highest importance, but one where beauty exists for its own sake: "The aesthetic faculties of the human soul have also been foreshadowed in the infinite Mind."

The following passage demonstrates how much Huxley was still under the influence of *Natural Theology:* "Regard a case of birds, or of butterflies [he writes] or examine the shell of an echinus, or a group of foramanifera, sifted out of the first handful of sea sand. Is it to be supposed for a moment that the beauty or outline and colour of the first, the geometrical regularity of the second, or the extreme variety and elegance of the third, are any *good* to the animals?"[23]

Seeing nature as a poem rather than a machine leads him to an attempted refutation of Cuvier's laws of correlation, which the French scientist employed in reconstructing extinct vertebrate forms. Huxley's was, at best, an ill-considered criticism; his experience with fossils went back only two years, but Cuvier had been remarkably successful in reconstruction of extinct animals largely because he recognized the significance of adaptation of a creature's organism to its environment. In any case, the lecture brought a letter of rebuke from Darwin and a published rebuttal from Hugh Falconer, a reputable paleontologist. The air was beginning to be marked by no little tension. Did England's scientists sense that it would only be one short step from attacking Cuvier to attacking his foremost English disciple—Sir Richard Owen?

VI *Controversy with Owen*

Huxley's most significant scientific paper prior to the publication of the *Origin* was "The Theory of the Vertebrate Skull,"[24] the Royal Society's Croomian Lecture, which he delivered in June, 1858. In addition to being a pioneering work in vertebrate morphology, the paper marked his entrance into the theater of public controversy—a locale in which, until his death thirty-seven years later, he was to be a familiar figure and a star performer.

Men of perception and discretion ultimately recognized Huxley as a dangerous man with whom to disagree; and many, no matter how strongly they opposed his views, either expressed their differences diplomatically or refrained from making them public. Huxley was formidable in controversy partly because he was not given to speaking publicly without first making sure of his ground and partly because he was in command of a literary style which not only combined plain statement with a biting rhetoric but also, at times, could be disconcertingly personal in its tone. His fierce and forceful retorts have been remembered long after the more or less innocuous replies of his adversaries were forgotten. The wonder today is that so many otherwise able men in England were willing to engage him on his own ground and with weapons of which he was unquestionably a master.

Sir Richard Owen, who has the dubious distinction of being the first notable public figure to trace a sharp decline in his reputation to an unfortunate encounter with Professor Huxley, was conceded in his day to be England's foremost paleontologist and comparative anatomist. In 1858, Owen was the Director of the British Museum; and his extensive work on fossils had earned him the title "the British Cuvier." He was not, however, well liked in scientific circles. He seems to have been in the habit of browbeating his colleagues and was not above forcing them to accept questionable theories and data ("an autocrat of the natural sciences," Leonard Huxley has called him). He was, moreover, something of an intriguer who wielded his influence to increase his own reputation rather than the cause of scientific truth. A protégé of Prince Albert, Owen was as proud of his court connections as of his work as a scientist.

One of the doctrines Owen had succeeded in forcing upon his colleagues was an idealistic view of vertebrate anatomy. When Huxley returned to England in 1850, he naturally enough fell under the influence of Owen. But even at this time he seems to have had some reservations toward Owen's scientific capabilities. "Owen is an able man, but to my mind not so great as he thinks himself," he wrote to a fellow scientist in 1851. "He can only work in the concrete from bone to bone, in abstract reasoning he becomes lost. . . ."[25] An incident took place in 1856 which Owen in later years had good reason to regret. Upon being invited to give a series of lectures at the Royal School of Mines, he assumed the title Professor of Paleontology, a move which Huxley interpreted as a reflection on his own work since he was at the time the institution's acknowledged fossil expert. When Owen made no attempt to justify this unusual procedure, Huxley broke all relations with him. And, as his opinion of Owen's character began to decline, so did his respect for the man as a scientist. "What a capital title that is they give him of the British Cuvier," Huxley wrote to Sir Joseph Hooker two years later. "He stands in exactly the same relation to the French as British brandy to cognac."[26]

One of the more interesting aspects of this controversy is the fact that the *ad hominem* element was very much present. As later events were to demonstrate, Huxley could be amiable and tolerant in the company of those with whom he disagreed; and at various times during his career he found himself differing with Herbert Spencer, Charles Kingsley, Darwin, and Lyell on some very serious and fundamental questions of science and theology. But these differences never brought out the warrior in him. Huxley's major controversies—those with William Gladstone, the Duke of Argyll, certain orthodox churchmen, and Owen—were different; for in these instances he was dealing with persons he frankly disliked. And when, in 1857, Owen read a paper before the Linnaean Society which contained numerous observations on the cranial formation of the genus *Homo* that were sharply at variance with those of Huxley, the stage was set for a controversy that ultimately shook England's scientific establishment to its foundations.

Shortly thereafter Huxley, whose work up to this time had been with invertebrates, undertook a personal investigation into questions of development and vertebrate anatomy. These were the findings that were incorporated in the Croomian Lecture.

Since the paper had as one of its primary objectives the demolition of many of Owen's fondest assumptions concerning vertebrate anatomy, its delivery on this occasion was a deft combination of insult and injury since Owen himself was presiding at the meeting. In Huxley's prefatory remarks he refers to those "writers on the theory of the vertebrate skull who have given a retrograde impulse to inquiry, and have thrown obscurity and confusion on that which twenty years ago had been made plain and clear." There were few among the scientific assembly who could not know that these remarks were specifically directed at the chair.

Huxley's paper attempted to demonstrate that the skull and the vertebrate column are organized along radically differing principles, rather than being modifications of such a unifying principle as that which, for example, is to be discovered in the bodily organization of the lobster. Huxley concedes that, at an early stage of development, there is some "primitive identity of structure"; but, in their adult forms, their principles of organization are markedly different. Owen had advocated a theory—one derived largely from the writings of Lorenz Oken—that the skull was composed of three modified vertebrae, complete even to a strict parallel between the subsidiary head bones and limbs attached to the spine. According to Huxley, however, it is no more true to say the skull is a modified vertebrae than it is to "affirm that the vertebrae column was a modified skull."

Besides giving a new direction to work in vertebrate development and formally liberating British anatomists from the restricting views of Owen, Huxley's lecture also raised serious questions concerning the theory of archetypes borrowed by Owen from Cuvier. In establishing his case for human anatomy, Huxley demonstrated logical parallels in the anatomical makeup of an ostrich, a turtle, a carp, and a sheep; and he was well on his way to perceiving that one plan unites, if not all living things, all forms of animal life.

Huxley was by this time moving in the same direction as Darwin. He was soon to jettison the archetype theory altogether and ultimately to adopt, as we have seen, an "agnostic" attitude toward the question of species. This line of investigation within five years was to carry him to *Man's Pace in Nature,* which was more advanced than even Darwin's ideas; even the *Origin of Species* did not apply the concept of organic evolution to man.

CHAPTER 2

Origin, *Oxford, Orthodoxy*

THE *Origin of Species,* the book which was destined to give an entirely new direction to Huxley's activities, made its appearance as a small, green volume on November 24, 1859. For some time previously—or ever since the reading the previous year[1] of the Darwin-Wallace paper on natural selection before the Linnaean Society—Huxley had made it a point to refrain from commenting on the species question per se. A lecture which he gave at the Royal Institution in June, 1859 (published in expanded form in *Macmillan's Magazine* the following December), reveals him, however, as already having assumed the role of an advocate for Darwin. "On the Persistent Forms of Animal Life" is an attempt to explain how certain forms—the Nautilus, the Crocodillia, and the Globigerina—have persisted for millions of years without any essential alteration. Advance and change, Huxley says, take place only when aided by the environment; evolution does not presuppose that variation is universal. It will be remembered that he had posed this very same question five years before in his review of *The Vestiges* to invalidate the evolutionary arguments of Chambers.

Huxley did not, therefore, become an official convert to Darwinism until reading the book itself. This appears somewhat strange in retrospect since he had for some time been familar with the ideas of Darwin in their general outline, but one of Huxley's characteristics was, as has been noted, that he always proceeded cautiously and never failed to make sure of his ground before accepting any new intellectual position. This characteristic gave many of his ideas their permanence and stood him in excellent stead in his many controversies. So far as the *Origin* was concerned, it was the eminently scientific approach of Darwin—the vast quantity of evidence with which he supported his ideas, and the masterful manner in which he ticked off his points—that made Huxley an immediate and enthusiastic convert.

In a letter of November, 1859 to Darwin, written shortly after reading the *Origin,* Huxley conveyed his admiration, announced his conversion, and warned of the hostile reception the theories could count on receiving from the public. "Depend on it," he said, "you have earned the lasting gratitude of all thoughtful men. And as to the curs which will bark and yelp, you must recollect that some of your friends . . . may stand you in good stead. I am sharpening up my claws and beak in readiness."[2] Huxley's opportunity to put them to use was not long in coming.

I   *Darwin's Bulldog*

On December 26, an unsigned review of the *Origin*—enthusiastic and knowledgeable—appeared in the London *Times.* Most of the newspaper's book reviews were written by staff members, and the fact that the reviewer could have read Darwin's book, grasped the pith of his argument, and spoken so forthrightly on the subject just a month after publication must have given pause to readers whose minds were not too blunted after Christmas dinner to consider the problem. In scientific circles much speculation occurred as to who had written the review: most concluded that such a review could only have been written by a trained scientist; others reasoned—correctly—that it could only have been written by Huxley.

Not until many years later did Huxley describe the lucky chance that had given him the opportunity to strike this telling blow for Darwin. The editor of the book column, Samuel Lucas, had received a review copy of the *Origin;* but, being untrained in science, he was forced to acknowledge his incompetence to give the work a fair reading; and, in looking around for someone to do the job, he had been recommended to employ Huxley. Huxley leaped at the opportunity, as he later wrote, to force "the educated mob who derive their ideas from the *Times*" to show some respect for Darwin. The review did much to secure a fair hearing for the *Origin.*[3]

Huxley immediately saw that Darwin's explanation of "natural selection" thoroughly disposed of what he had considered to be the chief objection to evolutionary theory: why evolution had occurred in some groups and not in others. Of course, it also disposed of most of the other suppositions—scientific and theological—which had previously stood opposed to it. In his review Huxley attempts to discredit such widely held scientific beliefs as the archetypal theory and the geological theory of catastrophism. He casts doubt on the archetypal theory by questioning whether species are, in the last analysis, definable or, indeed, anything more than "an abstraction of the intellect." Huxley's reservations toward the doctrine of Final Causes, as articulated by William Paley, has its sources in the fact that there are creatures who have rudimentary eyes who cannot see and others with wings who cannot fly. As for the account of creation contained in Genesis, it is bypassed as not being "capable of discussion by reason."

In awarding Huxley the Darwin Medal in 1894, Lord Kelvin, at one time one of Darwin's most troublesome critics, commented acutely on the manner in which Huxley had conducted himself as the advocate of evolution: "That advocacy had one striking mark; while it made or strove to make clear how deep the new view went down, and how far it reached, he never shrank from trying to make equally clear the limit beyond which it should not go."[4]

Huxley was proud of this aspect of his work on behalf of Darwin, and even in the *Times* review he emphasized the impossibility of affirming "either the truth or falsehood of Mr. Darwin's views at the present stage of inquiry." Indeed, Huxley was so reluctant to overstate the scientific support for the theory that he brought up points, or at least one that Darwin thought to be an insignificant cavil; for Huxley contended that Darwin's theory could not be proven beyond question until selective breeding from the same stock produced species sterile with one another. This reservation, according to Darwin, failed to give adequate recognition to the fact of partial fertility among varieties produced by artificial selection.

In "The Origin of Species"[5]—a more detailed account of Darwin's ideas than the *Times* article, and one that appeared in the *Westminster Review* for April, 1860—Huxley describes the controversy that had been created by the *Origin:* "Everybody has read Mr. Darwin's book, or at least, has given an opinion upon its merits or demerits; pietists, whether lay or ecclesiastic, decry

it with the mild railing which sounds so charitable; bigots de-
nounce it with ignorant invective; old ladies of both sexes consider it a decidedly dangerous book, and even savants, who have
no better mud to throw, quote antiquated writers to show that its
author is no better than an ape himself."[6]

This *Westminster* article was an attempt by Huxley to give an
intelligible explanation "of the established facts connected with
species, and of the relation of the explanation of those facts offered by Mr. Darwin ... to the requirements of scientific logic."
Within each species there are two tendencies: one to minor variation and one to general similarity. A gradual process of successive variations leads ultimately to the formation of a new species.
Since the science of genetics was still unknown, Huxley was forced
to admit that scientists could not say what the cause of these minor variations was. But that they, indeed, occurred was an established fact; and Huxley cites numerous cases advanced by Darwin to illustrate how variation actually takes place.

In his review for the *Times,* Huxley spoke of Darwin's being
"as greedy of cases and precedents as any constitutional lawyer."
But while Darwin's thoroughness was his strongest point and
made a public not disposed toward accepting his ideas consider
them in spite of itself, it was at the same time a barrier to the
ordinary reader. "*The Origin of Species* is by no means an easy
book to read," Huxley wrote, "if by reading is implied the full
comprehension of an author's meaning." The number of readers
who have discovered this firsthand are legion. When one considers the large number of scientists (Sir Richard Owen, for example) and brilliant amateurs (Samuel Wilberforce, for example) who did not demonstrate comprehension in their early
writings on the *Origin,* one realizes the importance of Huxley's
role in making the theory comprehensible to the ordinary citizen.

II "*Great is humbug ...*"

Huxley's next defense of Darwin was not in print but on the
platform. Slightly more than six months had passed since the
publication of the *Origin* when the British Association for the
Advancement of Science convened at Oxford for its annual meeting in June, 1860. Darwin himself was sick and unable to attend,
but he was represented at the three-day meeting by two of his

most capable supporters—Huxley and Sir Joseph Hooker. Sir Richard Owen was on hand as a spokesman for the anti-evolutionary faction of English science; and giving support to Sir Richard was the Bishop of Oxford himself, Samuel Wilberforce, who was known to the university's undergraduates as "Soapy Sam" because of his superb oratorical powers. A good-sized crowd had converged on Oxford to witness the proceedings; it was being whispered about that Bishop Wilberforce intended to employ his rhetoric in the service of orthodoxy and, if possible, "smash Darwin."

No one was surprised when quite early in the proceedings of the first day a statement by Owen provoked a rebuke from Huxley. Sir Richard, ever the foe of evolution, made the very leading statement that the brain of the gorilla resembled that of man less than it did "the very lowest and most problematical of the Quadrumana." Huxley knew that the crowd, a partisan group composed of distinguished scientists, well-dressed ladies, anxious clergymen, and raucous undergraduates, was hardly the public before which an impartial scientific discussion could be carried on; and he contented himself with giving Owen's contention a direct contradiction and once again took his seat.[7] Huxley was understandably nettled after this run-in with Owen. He had intended to leave Oxford on Friday evening since, as he remarked, he had no desire to be "episcopally pounded" on Saturday; but he was persuaded to stay on by Robert Chambers. The Saturday meeting was so well attended (upwards of seven hundred people) that it was moved to the Library of the Museum.

When on Saturday Bishop Wilberforce at last received his opportunity to speak, he held forth on the theories of Darwin for, as one observer put it, "a full half hour, with inimitable spirit, emptiness, and unfairness." Bishop Wilberforce's firsthand knowledge of science was slight, and his talk was of little value as a contribution to knowledge. But the Bishop's avowed intention was not to evaluate the heresy but to squash it—and what better way to squash it than to ridicule it? And what would be more effective than to subject the humorless scientists to a merciless public ribbing? By anybody's standards his talk was both witty and entertaining in the extreme.[8]

Estimates of the Bishop's tone vary. According to Francis Dar-

win, he ridiculed Darwin badly and Huxley savagely. F. W. Farrar's impression of the talk, however, was that it was "flippant
and unscientific rather than insolent, vulgar, or personal," which
seems more likely. It is improbable that the urbane Bishop of
Oxford—who doubtless considered Darwin and Huxley to be up-
starts rather than men of genuine learning, and their doctrine
a nonsensical aberration rather than a far-reaching, well-docu-
mented scientific theory—needed, while speaking to an audience
sympathetic with his own views, to harangue them in a "savage,"
or even remotely savage, fashion for half an hour.[9] Only in his
peroration, Dean Farrar felt, did Wilberforce adopt a personal
tone. Turning to Huxley, he inquired blandly whether he traced
his gorilla heritage from his grandfather or his grandmother.
Shortly thereafter, he concluded his talk and sat down.

When Huxley slowly, almost reluctantly, arose to speak, his
gravity presented a distinct contrast to the flippancy of the Bishop. He felt, he said, no shame at having an ape for a grandfather: "If there were an ancestor whom I should feel shamed on
recalling, it would rather be a man, a man of restless and versa-
tile intellect, who, not content with an equivocal success in
his own sphere of activity plunges into scientific questions with
which he has no real acquaintance, only to obscure them by an
aimless rhetoric and distract the attention of his hearers from
the real point at issue by eloquent digressions and skilled appeals to religious prejudice."[10] There could be no doubt in
anybody's mind at whom Huxley had aimed his remark.

When Huxley first rose to speak, there had been only a smat-
tering of applause. The immediate effect of his reply upon the
audience had been one of surprise and shock; in fact, one lady
actually fainted and had to be borne bodily from the auditorium. As Huxley continued to speak, gravely and in measured
tones, the audience was moved, in spite of itself, to murmurs of
approval. "Darwin's theory," he said, "was an explanation of
phenomena in natural history, as the undulatory theory was of
the phenomena of light. No one objected to *that* theory because
an undulation of light had never been arrested and measured."
As he continued to tick off his points, the audience was moved to
giving its involuntary assent. Was the Darwinian hypothesis a
proven fact? No, it wasn't. But it offered scientists their best

explanation to that time of the species question. The impression conveyed to the audience was that Huxley was indeed a humble seeker after truth. When Huxley once again took his seat, the applause was hardly less than that which had greeted the Bishop.

Forgetting the dramatic aspects of Huxley's reply, one should look closely at the ideas themselves; for there is, in fact, something paradoxical in Huxley's stand. His insistence that the ideas of Darwin are in no case to be accepted as proven facts comes as a surprise when one considers the warmth with which he states his case. On the one hand, in his many articles on the subject he denounces those who believe in Genesis because they accept the doctrine without demanding evidence. Yet, on the other hand, what he is asking his audience to believe—evolution by natural selection—he readily grants is itself only a theory. The fossil record at that time was scanty, and however confident Huxley himself may have been that time would produce evidence which would prove the truth of the theory, he had no right to expect the rest of the world to immediately embrace evolution on this account. The strong manner in which Huxley in the next few years was to state the case for Darwinism and against Genesis may have had the effect of persuading the uncommitted, but it was certainly not warranted by the evidence.

Nothing was proved at Oxford, and the events there were only an inconclusive minor skirmish in the Genesis contra Darwin controversy, a conflict which has, in fact, not yet been resolved to everyone's satisfaction. The real issue at stake was something else. With the possible exceptions of the work of Copernicus and Galileo in the seventeenth century, science had never—nor has it since—produced a theory which stood in such direct contradiction to the teachings of established religion. In fact, the real point at issue was: Are scientists to be allowed genuine freedom of inquiry?

And Jacques Barzun has pointed out some of the contradictions in Huxley's own approach to the question. "From the very first," Barzun writes, "he held against the completeness of the theory the fact that it lacked experimental proof. Until from a common stock varieties could be produced which were infertile when crossed together (for only then would one have seen species originate) Huxley was not satisfied with the Darwinian theory. He saw no reason to change between 1860 and 1887 when he reverted to the problem."[11] Even the most ardent and devoted Darwinian had serious reservations about the scientific questions involved. What Huxley really wanted was freedom for science to pursue the subject without having recourse to either civil or clerical authority.

Most laymen in 1860 were still only vaguely aware of the meaning of such phrases as "evolution," "natural selection," and "descent with modification." They did know, however, that implications of Darwin's theories were in contradiction to the accounts of creation found in Genesis. As a result, talk for a long time centered about the proceedings at Oxford rather than about the ideas themselves. Huxley's review of the *Origin* in the *Times* the previous December had caused no great stir among the public. And, if only a small portion of the newspaper's readers had taken the trouble to wade through Huxley's article, an even smaller number had read and understood the *Origin* itself. For this reason, if Wilberforce and Owen had succeeded in their attempt to discredit evolutionary speculation and its advocates, the cause could have been set back many years. Public ignorance and apathy would have done the rest.

A century later, the idea that any outside authority—civil or clerical—might aspire to impose an arbitrary restraint upon scientific investigation is unthinkable. Today, scientists enjoy a freedom heretofore unknown and, after a fashion, are looked upon as spokesmen for Truth in the same way theologians were in former times. It was at the Oxford meeting, however, that science first was able to effectively serve public notice that it intended to go its own way unhampered by limitations imposed by outside authority.

As far as Huxley himself was concerned, the Oxford meeting had the unforeseen effect of making him the unofficial spokesman for English science; and, during the next thirty-five years, this role was to consume most of his energies. "Great is humbug and it will prevail unless those who do not like it will hit hard," Huxley was later to declare; and few hit harder in this respect than Professor Huxley (as he soon came to be known). In countless lectures, essays, and books, he subjected most of the flabby and complacent aspects of English life to a merciless bombardment, frequently not unlike the pasquinades of Jonathan Swift. More and more of his time was spent on the lecture platform and less in the laboratory. Wherever he spoke, Huxley could be assured of an eager and enthusiastic audience, and his books and pamphlets sold as well as novels.

Moreover, since he was good newspaper copy, there were always reporters on hand to carry his words and ideas to an even wider audience. As a diplomat, "wire-puller," and administrator, he was to prove no less successful than as an original investigator. Impossible to ignore, his success was enormous; and his influence was incalculable. He made it a point to miss no opportunities in the decades to come to aid the cause of science, and the name "Professor Huxley" not only came to be familiar to every literate Englishman but became a synonym for the militant spirit of British science itself.

III *Man's Place in Nature*

Huxley delivered yet another popular exposition of the ideas of Darwin when, in the fall of 1862, he addressed a series of six lectures to workingmen at the School of Mines. These lectures, never rewritten by Huxley—indeed, never written down by him at all—were transcribed by an observer and published in pamphlet form under the title *On Our Knowledge of the Causes of the Phenomena of Organic Nature.* Their imperfections, however, did not keep them from enjoying a wide success in both England and the United States. Huxley, whose financial situation was still precarious and who the following year found it necessary to hock his Royal Society Gold Medal, had not foreseen the interest these discourses would attract; and he later expressed regret that he had not arranged their publication himself and thereby shared in their considerable commercial success.

Darwin, who thought highly of these addresses, frequently urged Huxley to revise and expand them into a systematic treatment of evolutionary theory. Huxley, too, was not altogether unhappy with them; for, despite their imperfections, he included them, unaltered, in Volume II of his *Collected Essays.*[12] And, indeed, reading over these somewhat rough lectures, one does sense a quality not to be found in his more carefully composed efforts.

Such passages as the following give the twentieth-century reader a good idea of the informal flavor of Huxley's address and of what it must have been like to sit at the feet of one of Victorian England's most entertaining and inspiring speakers: "Few animals can be more familiar to you than that whose skeleton is shown on our diagram. You need not bother yourselves with this *'Equs caballus,'* written under it; that is only the Latin name of it, and does not make it any better. It simply means the common horse."[13] Using the "common horse" for his starting point, Huxley describes the animal's anatomy and morphology as a marvelous machine; and he proceeds to show how the fuel—grass and oats—makes the machine run and how, marvelous as it is, the body of the horse is just one of many equally remarkable manifestations of the natural world.

In the second lecture Huxley returns to the past to give a rough idea of what the earth was like in bygone epochs. In this trip into remote time with its description of the bottom of the sea as a repository of all manner of bizarre and fascinating arcana, there are foreshadowings of "On a Piece of Chalk," which he delivered to the workingmen of Norwich six years later. The third lecture attempts to illuminate the assumptions which underlie science and the methods by which scientists attempt to ascertain truth. "The same mode of reasoning," Huxley declares, "was employed by Newton and La Place in their endeavours to discover and define the causes of the movements of the heavenly bodies as you, with your own common sense, would employ to detect a burglar."

Lectures IV and V are, like the earlier articles written for the *Times* and *Westminster Review,* a compact exposition of the views of Darwin—so compact, in fact, that Darwin was moved to write after having read them: "What is the good of my writing a thundering big book, when everything is in this green little book, so despicable for its size?"[14] Lecture VI, an investigation of the legitimate objections that might be raised to the *Origin,* concludes with the prophetic thought that the book will "be the guide of biological and psychological speculation for the next three or four generations."

Huxley's most substantial—as well as his most spectacular and controversial—contribution to his campaign to win acceptance for evolutionary doctrine was his book *Evidence as to Man's Place in Nature* (later shortened to *Man's Place in Nature*).[15] Published in January, 1863, three years after the *Origin,* it was also Huxley's first book. Huxley's earlier essays on the *Origin* were, to be sure, marvelous propaganda and popularization; *Man's Place,* however, the first work (forgetting the unscientific *Vestiges*) to attempt to relate man to the rest of the animal world within the framework of evolutionary theory, was an extension of the ideas of Darwin. A scientific, literary, and commercial success, as well as a *succés de scandale, Man's Place* is regarded today as a classic of English science—as a worthy rival to Newton's *Principia,* to Harvey's *Movement of the Heart and Blood,* and to the *Origin* itself.

Huxley exhibited no small amount of courage in publishing on the subject of man's origins at this time. Even Darwin had scrupulously avoided any mention of man so far as evolution was concerned. "Light will be thrown on the origin of man and his history," was all the *Origin* had to say on the subject.[16] Attempts to impute to man what were considered to be low origins were universally frowned upon, and criticism would be forthcoming from scientific as well as theological quarters. (Years later Huxley remarked that, for his own part, he could see no difference "between being a modified ape or modified dirt.")

Carlyle, for example, never forgave Huxley for the book; and Huxley described its reception in the 1894 Preface to Volume VII of his *Collected Essays:* "The Boreas of criticism blew his hardest blasts of misrepresentation and ridicule for some years; and I was even as one of the wicked. Indeed, it surprises me, at times, to think how any one who had sunk so low could since have emerged into, at any rate, relative respectability."[17] But by 1887 he was able to write to his friend Edward Clodd that "all the propositions laid down in the wicked book, which was so well anathematised a quarter of a century ago, are now taught in the text books. What a droll world it is!"[18]

The truth is that the reception accorded *Man's Place* was not nearly so hostile as might have been anticipated. When Huxley delivered a lecture in 1862 in Edinburgh on "The Relation of

Man to the Rest of the Animal Kingdom" (later incorporated into Part II of *Man's Place*), the outcry had been great. But, if a year later Englishmen were not yet ready to embrace a simian ancestry, they were at least willing to investigate the possibility. The many pasquinades and burlesques that had greeted the controversy on the subject of simian and human brains between Owen and Huxley amply demonstrate that a good part of the public was more amused than horrified by the possibility. And even such a bastion of conservatism as the *Athenaeum* was comparatively mild in its criticism of *Man's Place;* Huxley's intention is to "degrade" man, the reviewer observed somewhat petulantly.

The criticism, if it had any really noticeable effect, served to stimulate rather than to retard sales. The book was first issued in an edition of one thousand copies, which were immediately sold out; it went into a second edition and was periodically reprinted for the next forty years. There was, in addition, an American edition and a translation into German. The eager response of the reading public is reflected in a remark in the *London Daily Telegraph* for April, 1863. "The works of Darwin and Huxley," according to the writer, "are being seized from the hands of Mudies' shopmen as if they were novels."[19]

So far as scientists were concerned, the findings of Huxley were immediately incorporated into the work of other investigators; and the book had the effect of giving a new direction to studies in comparative anatomy and, in effect, of laying the foundation for the modern study of anthropology. The eminent English anthropologist Sir Arthur Keith has succinctly expressed his own view of what Huxley had accomplished: "In writing *Man's Place in Nature* Huxley ... rendered a great service to knowledge, but of even greater moment was the victory he then won in the cause of liberty. Until Huxley appeared as their champion anthropologists scarcely dared to state the truth as they found it; when he had silenced theological opposition, they were free to apply to the study of man the same methods as they employed in the study of other animals."[20]

The book, in addition, succeeded in laying to rest a protracted and irksome controversy with Richard Owen on the question of the resemblance of the brain of the gorilla to that of man. There are, in fact, two or three veiled sneers at Owen in the text: for example, a reference to the "surpassing courage" of the enunciator of a doctrine that is "directly negatived by the testimony of all original inquirers." It had been Owen, of course, who—however unwittingly—had supplied the initial momentum for the research that was to culminate in *Man's Place*. His paper read before the Linnaean Society in 1857, it is to be recalled, led Huxley to undertake his own investigations into development and vertebrate anatomy.

The interest in *Man's Place in Nature* today is, perhaps, primarily historical; but in many respects it continues to be as good an introduction to the subject of anthropology as has been written. There is a tendency for scientific works to date rapidly as new discoveries make old data obsolete, but such has not been the fate of *Man's Place*. Keith and Ashley Montague are only two of the twentieth-century anthropologists who have praised its continuing significance as a work of science. And the literary gifts of Huxley invested it with a readability that continues undiminished.

The first of the three sections into which the book is divided is entitled "The Natural History of the Man-Like Apes." In it Huxley makes a thorough survey of the reliable knowledge then current of the "man-like" apes gathered by naturalists in the field. It begins with such abstruse materials as the notes gathered by Edwardo Lopez, a sixteenth-century Portuguese sailor, and the first edition of the well-known *Purchas his Pilgrimage, or Relations of the World and the Religions observed in all Ages* (1619) by Samuel Purchas.

Huxley demonstrates how these often haphazard and unscientific observations nevertheless point to the conclusion that distinct genera of manlike apes are native to various parts of the world: the orangutan and the gibbon from eastern Asia; chimpanzees and gorillas from western Africa. Huxley's study was useful to scientists since he has extracted the pertinent information from a great deal of material and commented tellingly upon its value. It derives its literary merit from the arresting material it deals with and the masterly manner in which it is presented.

Huxley concludes this section by demonstrating the various

ways in which apes may be said to resemble man in their living habits. Various species of gibbon, for example, take to the erect posture without any apparent difficulty; but the orangutan moves about on all fours and never stands on its hind legs. Both types of Asian anthropoids are possessed of voices louder than those of any man, and both build nests in which to sleep. Moving to the African animals, Huxley notes that, although the chimpanzee occasionally takes to its hind legs, it cannot stand fully erect and moves about most often on all fours. The gorilla, on the other hand, is inclined to the erect posture, walks in a somewhat stooped manner, and moves on occasion by placing its arms on the ground and jumping forward. The voice of the chimpanzee is hoarse and not very loud; that of the gorilla is shrill and piercing. Like the Asian animals, those of Africa also build nests before retiring.

Huxley's versatility served him well in this undertaking. In the second section, "The Relations of Man to the Lower Animals," he argues man's resemblances from the standpoint of embryology. Prior to Darwin, it was generally conceded that there were no significant points at which man can be said to resemble, say, a dog. Certainly there are overwhelming differences between the body of a dog and that of a man. The developing embryos of both, however, offer many points of comparison. Huxley demonstrates that in its early stages the dog's embryo develops along lines very similar to those followed by that of a human. Embryology, indeed, supports the resemblance of man not only to apes but to all other vertebrates, including snakes, frogs and fishes. "Without question," Huxley writes, "the mode of origin and the early stages of the development of man are identical with those of the animals immediately below him on this scale; and without a doubt, in these respects, he is far nearer the apes than the apes are to the dog." Indeed, the development of the human ovum and that of the dog is so similar that they are for a long time indistinguishable. At the point they become distinguishable, however, it is still not possible to make any distinction between the developing human and the developing ape. Huxley's conclusion: the structural unity of man and the rest of the animal world, particularly with respect to the ape, is beyond argument.

Huxley proceeds from here to investigate the resemblances between men and anthropoid apes in respect to overall anatomical organization. Since the gorilla of all the anthropoid apes most resembles man, Huxley (using a measurement system of his own devising) demonstrates that in respect to relative proportions the limbs of the gorilla are closer in size to those of man than they are to those of other apes. In the average length of their legs, for example, those of the gibbon are greater than man almost as much as those of man are greater than the legs of the gorilla. Man, therefore, stands between the gorilla and the gibbon in this respect. Other measurements demonstrate that the size of the gorilla's legs, arms, hands, and feet are far closer to those of man than to those of other apes such as the "spider" monkey and the Indri. And the same conclusion is borne out in the investigation of the backbone, ribs, and pelvis of man, gorilla, and the other apes. There are, to be sure, many significant points of departure between man and gorilla; but equally significant differences obtain between the gorilla and the other apes. At this point the reader is already clear as to the main premise of the book: the physiological differences between the higher apes and man are less than the distinctions between the former group and the lower apes.

A large portion of the book is given over to debunking one of the beliefs then current about the unique anatomical organization of man. Many of them, preposterous as they seem today, had strong support in scientific circles. Many, indeed, had been personally fostered by Britain's leading comparative anatomist, Sir Richard Owen. Two premises in particular had been advanced by Owen in support of his recommendation that man be placed in a distinct order within the primates: first, man has hands and feet while all the apes possess four hands; and, second, the brain of man exhibits certain structures unknown in that of the ape. Why many anatomists subscribed to the former proposition is perfectly understandable. In externals the feet and hands of man differ widely. However, an investigation of the bone structure of the ape reveals the foot of the ape to be remarkably similar to the foot of man—differing, Huxley writes, only in "proportions, in the degree of mobility, and in the secondary arrangements of the parts."

Huxley had foreseen that his revolutionary findings would be the subject of misrepresentation. The following passage was deliberately aimed at forestalling any criticism that he was nothing more than apologist for Darwin, and it clearly shows the position he held on the "question of questions." "Let me take this opportunity then of distinctly asserting," Huxley writes, near the conclusion of Part II, "that every bone of a gorilla bears marks by which it might be distinguished from the corresponding bone of a man; and that, in the present creation, at any rate, no intermediate link bridges over the gap between Homo and Troglodytes."

Paleontology was a young science a century ago. The two most significant finds in 1863 were two skull fragments—one in the valley of the Mense in 1832; the other in the Neander valley near Düsseldorf in 1857. In the third section, "Fossil Remains of Man," Huxley examines these particular remains and argues his basic premise from the standpoint of paleontology.

The question Huxley sets out to answer concerning the two fossil skulls follows from Part Two: Do these findings in any manner fill the requirements of a structural link between man and manlike apes? The Engis skull does not, for its characteristics are very similar to those of the skulls of the various races throughout the world at the present time. The Neanderthal skull, however, possesses many pithecoid characteristics, in combination with a large brain case—a size about equal to that of the average Polynesian or Hottentot. "In no sense, then," Huxley cautiously concludes, "can the Neanderthal bones be regarded as the remains of a human being intermediate between Men and Apes. At most they demonstrate the existence of a man whose skull may be said to revert somewhat to pithecoid type." Huxley nowhere states that man was descended from apes or monkeys—only from stock common to both.

Huxley's era was the last in which one man could master a variety of scientific disciplines. Most of the conclusions drawn from his paleontological data continue to be accepted today by anthropologists without significant alteration. The only difference is one knows more. One can, for example, date fossils and have a reasonably certain idea of the epoch in which man emerged. And the great number of fossils gathered in the last century have uncovered specimens exhibiting both pithecoid and anthropoid characteristics. Anthropologists may indeed have uncovered in Australopithecus Africanus man's immediate forebear, but there is no escaping that *Man's Place* laid the foundation for anthropological investigation in the intervening years by directing the attention of scientists to the resemblances between men and apes and by posing questions concerning the existence of an "intermediate" or "missing" link.

That there are immense qualitative differences between men and animals Huxley was well aware; he did not wish to de-emphasize them, nor did he wish to undertake the role of an un-questioning advocate of evolutionary doctrine that was blind to man's moral capacities, his unique intelligence, and his capacity for unselfish, even altruistic, activity. The conclusion to the second part of *Man's Place in Nature* in which Huxley refers to man as "the great Alps and Andes of the living world" is perhaps as eloquent a testament of belief in the nobler aspects of man's being as has ever been written: "Thoughtful men, once es-caped from the blinding influences of traditional prejudice, will find in the lowly stock whence Man has sprung, the best evi-dence of the splendour of his capacities; and will discern in his long progress through the Past, a reasonable ground of faith in his attainment of a nobler Future."[21]

IV *The New Orthodoxy*

With the passage of time, the clouds of misrepresentation, misunderstanding, and abuse that had originally threatened to engulf the *Origin* began to lift. A list of those scientists who had publicly recorded their reservations toward evolutionary doc-trine within months of the publication of the *Origin* reads like a roll call of the distinguished scientists of Europe and America: Louis Agassiz, the American biologist; William Henry Harvey, the Irish botanist; François Pictet, the Swiss paleontologist; and, at home, Adam Sedgwick, the geologist and Thomas Wallaston, the zoologist, as well as Owen. Younger men were enlisting un-der the Darwinian banner in large numbers; older naturalists, per-haps, remained wary of giving wholehearted support to Darwin.

In retrospect, considering the heretical nature of the *Origin* and its heavy emphasis on utility and struggle, the ready acceptance accorded to Darwinian theory is startling. "Darwin is conquering everywhere," Charles Kingsley wrote in 1863 to F. D. Maurice, "and rushing in like a flood, by the mere force of truth and fact."[22] Victory by this time was already assured; in a few years it would be complete. By 1880, in fact, the wheel had come full circle. Speaking in that year to an audience at the Royal Institution, Huxley was moved to comment with a deep irony on the unquestioning acceptance being accorded to Darwin:

> History warns us, however, that it is the customary fate of new truths to begin as heresies and to end as superstitions; and, as matters now stand, it is hardly rash to anticipate that, in another twenty years, the new generation, educated under the influences of the present day, will be in danger of accepting the main doctrines of the "Origin of Species," with as little reflection, and it may be with as little justification, as so many of our contemporaries, twenty years ago, rejected them.[23]

The last occasion on which Huxley found it necessary to employ his "claws and beak" in defense of Darwin was in 1864. English critics by this time had developed some discretion in subjecting Darwin to their invective, and in this instance the attack originated across the channel. Huxley's article "Criticisms on the 'Origin of Species',"[24] which appeared in the *Natural History Review*, was written in reply to two books: *On the Darwinian Theory* by Rudolf Kölliker, the German histologist; and *On Examinations of Darwin's Origin of Species* by M. J. P. Flourens, a French physiologist and, like Owen, a former student of Cuvier. Kölliker was guilty of certain misapprehensions respecting Darwin, most especially of having attributed to Darwin a teleological belief that he never intended. Huxley found much in Kölliker's monograph that was worthy of praise, but his reaction to the book of Flourens was of a decidedly different nature.

The French scientist had attacked Darwin in language that would have done even an Owen or a Wilberforce proud. The *Origin,* according to Flourens, was a repository of "obscure ideas" and of "superannuated personifications" couched in "pretentious and empty language." This attack led Huxley to reply in a similarly outspoken vein. "Such language is," Huxley writes, "preposterous, and incompatible with anything but absolute ignorance of the best established facts.... We should have passed it over in silence had it not appeared to afford some clue to M. Flourens' unhesitating, a priori repudiation of all forms of the progressive modification of living beings."

Huxley's review brought an enthusiastic letter of approval from Darwin, but later events suggest it might have been better had Huxley followed his original inclination to pass the book over in silence and let it find its deserved oblivion. Flourens, who doubtless inherited his distaste for evolutionary speculation from Cuvier, was at the time the perpetual Secretary of the French Academy of Sciences; and it is perhaps more than coincidence that the academy subsequently effected a conspiracy of silence respecting the ideas of Darwin which continued for two decades. Six years later, in 1870, a candidature in the academy for Darwin was rejected; and, when he was finally admitted in 1878, it was for his work in botany. Huxley's review was a factor, though not the only one, that retarded the spread of evolutionary theory in France.

After 1864 Huxley's interests moved away from evolution proper to scientific questions of a more general nature, as well as into the realm of education. When subsequently he did write on evolution—as in his review of Ernst Haeckel's *The Natural History of Creation* in 1869 and in his article "Mr. Darwin's Critics"[25] in 1871—he was trying to correct misapprehensions respecting Darwin's ideas rather than to defend them against the witless attacks of partisan critics. In the latter article, which appeared in the *Contemporary Review,* he declares that the "ignorance and insolence" which characterized most of the early attacks on Darwin had all but disappeared. "Instead of abusive nonsense," he writes, "we now read essays which are, at worst, more or less intelligent and appreciative; while, sometimes ... they have a real and permanent value."

But, even as critical comment became more temperate and as the theory gained wider acceptance, new problems began to arise. Evolution began to be advanced as the basis for all kinds of teleological philosophies, most of which held that man was evolving toward some kind of super creature in accordance with a predesigned plan. Huxley, predictably, was squarely opposed to such scientifically unsupportable views. "The theory of evolution is the most formidable opponent of all the commoner and coarser forms of teleology," he wrote in 1869 in his review of Haeckel's book. Teleological interpretations of evolutionary doctrine, Huxley felt, ignored one of the basic ideas of Darwin: organic change is the result of a *chance* combination of heredity and environment. Huxley did not feel that the state of scientific knowledge was such that anyone could predict the directions life could take.

If there were, indeed, a higher plan (Huxley thought the discussion was academic), man could not know what it was in any case. He gives the analogy of a deathwatch living in a clock case:

Listening to the monotonous "tick! tick!" so exactly like his own, he might arrive at the conclusion that the clock was itself a monstrous sort of death-watch, and that its final cause and purpose was to tick. How easy to point to the clear relation of the whole mechanism to the pendulum, to the fact that the one thing the clock did always and without intermission was to tick and that all the rest of its phenomena were intermittent and subordinate to ticking![26]

Broad Church clergymen and theologically inclined laymen, meanwhile, were attempting to harmonize the findings of science with Holy Writ, with the inevitable result that both science and religion were distorted. St. George Mivart, the biologist, was so anxious to resolve the apparent contradictions of the new science and revealed religion that he even went so far as to say that evolution had for centuries been a cardinal principle of Roman Catholic dogma, citing as his authorities two notable scholastic philosophers—Thomas Aquinas and Father Suarez. Huxley replied to this surprising assertion in "Mr. Darwin's Critics" and in so doing assumed the role of "defender of Catholic orthodoxy."

Mivart in his book *The Genesis of Species* had written that many orthodox Roman Catholic theologians had distinctly asserted the possibility of "derivative creation" or "evolution"; and, in particular, they had advanced the name of Francisco Suarez, referring specifically to the Jesuit writer's Fifteenth Metaphysical Disputation. Huxley, after expressing his surprise that the Catholic Church as long ago as the seventeenth century had anticipated Darwin ("My astonishment reached its climax when I found Mr. Mivart citing Father Suarez as his chief witness in favor of the scientific freedom enjoyed by Catholics"), went to the works of Suarez. Only, however, to be "cruelly disappointed," for he was unable to discover any justification for Mivart's claim that Suarez had advocated a doctrine of evolution. Indeed, Mivart's authority was quite orthodox in his beliefs. Suarez supports the notion that the world was created in six days and that woman was created from the rib of man. "It is, in fact, impossible," Huxley concluded, "to admit that Suarez held any opinion respecting the origin of species, except such as is consistent with the strictest and most literal interpretation on the words of Genesis."

How firmly opposed Huxley was to this growing tendency to warp the ideas of Darwin is also illustrated in "Mr. Darwin's Critics." Huxley elequently states his own position concerning the conflicting accounts of creation advanced by Genesis and by science:

The present antagonism between theology and science does not arise from any assumption by the men of science that all theology must necessarily be excluded from science, but simply because they are unable to allow that reason and morality have two weights and two measures; and that the belief in a proposition, because authority tells you it is true, or because you wish to believe it, which is a high crime and misdemeanor when the subject matter of reasoning is of one kind, becomes under the alias of "faith" the greatest of all virtues when the subject matter of reasoning is of another kind.[27]

This statement is the most precise public one Huxley ever made respecting the conflict between Genesis and Darwin, although he had in the early 1860's argued the point in a moving series of letters with Charles Kingsley. Huxley remained throughout his life critical of, as he termed them, "putters of new wine into old bottles." Broad Church rationalizing was as offensive to him as it was to orthodox thinkers such as William Mallock—although for precisely the opposite reasons.

In the second section of the same essay Huxley attempts a defense of evolution against one of the sounder criticisms to be brought against it: Could the doctrine, as articulated by Darwin, account for the qualitative distinction that exists between animals and men? The question had been raised not only by

Mivart but also by Alfred Russell Wallace in a recently published collection of essays, *Contributions to the Theory of Natural Selection*. The emergence of Wallace as a critic of Darwinism was more than a little peculiar since it was he who, with Darwin, had co-authored the first statement of the principle of evolution through natural selection in a paper read before the Linnaean Society in 1858. Wallace and Mivart conceded the fact of species mutation, but they thought that chance evolution could not explain man's higher nature. To Mivart, divine intervention was necessary to account for man's soul; to Wallace, a higher intelligence had guided the evolution of man's brain.

Huxley attempts to answer these questionings with an argument similar to the one he later employed in "The Physical Basis of Life." He suggests that the distinction between man and animals was really only one of degree; animals, he avers, have emotions as well as powers of judgment. Concerning the larger question—has evolution produced in the consciousness of man a new factor which is independent of physical forces?—Huxley writes: "Consciousness and molecular actions are capable of being expressed by one another, just as heat and mechanical action are capable of being expressed by one another."

During the Victorian Age in England the hitherto haphazard accumulation of scientific data in many areas gave way to the systematized pursuit of knowledge. Two scientific disciplines which emerged in the early nineteenth century were geology and paleontology. As recently as the mid-eighteenth century geology had not been thought of as a systematic field of inquiry at all. The significance of fossils as a record of the history of past life on the earth was only beginning to be understood, while fossil collecting itself remained for the first three decades of the century largely the pursuit of untrained amateurs, many of whom were clergymen. Although Darwin had clearly stated the hypothesis of evolution, Huxley knew that a great deal of scientific work would need to be done before the manner in which organic change took place could be ascertained or verified. His influential addresses to scientific bodies attempted to bring home this truth of Darwinism to his fellow scientists.

In three lectures before the Geological Society—"Geological Contemporaneity" (1862), "Geological Reform" (1869), and

"Paleontology and Evolution" (1871)—Huxley evaluated the impact of the new biological discoveries on the twin sciences of paleontology and geology. In "Geological Contemporaneity" Huxley is sharply critical of the practices of geologists and of the disunity that exists within the young science. This criticism was in many ways justified since geologists were disunited partly because so many of them were clergymen, and this had the effect of dividing them on many fundamental assumptions of their science. The doctrine of "catastrophism," for example, though it was soon to be discredited, had many distinguished men among its adherents. And those geologists (mostly the younger men with no church connections), who had followed the lead of James Hutton and Sir Charles Lyell in embracing the uniformitarian concept of geologic time at the expense of the catastrophic cosmogony and Mosaic accounts of creation, were suddenly forced to reappraise their generous estimates of the antiquity of the earth sharply downward. In 1865 William Thomson (later Lord Kelvin) read a paper before the Royal Society, "The Doctrine of Uniformity in Geology Briefly Refuted," which reckoned the age of the earth at somewhere between twenty and forty million years.

Kelvin and his colleagues in a series of seemingly irrefutable experiments based their estimates of the age of the earth on the rate at which the crust was cooling, and they buttressed them with other calculations which reckoned that the planet in the not-too-distant past would have been too hot to support life. The fatal flaw in Kelvin's concept of the earth and sun—that they were cooling off after the fashion of a bowl of soup—would not be discovered for forty years. Not until the successful isolation of radium by the Curies, and their subsequent experiments demonstrating that it maintained its temperature independent of its surroundings, did scientists realize that a celestial body could maintain a constant temperature for unlimited time. Only in the twentieth century were geologists once again able to speak freely of the earth as having unlimited antiquity.

But the claims of Kelvin caused Darwin great distress; for evolution, as he conceived it, took place by slow, imperceptible changes, and it hardly seemed likely that life could have achieved its various stages of complexity in the short period of time allotted by the physicists. Darwin's letters reflect his dismay at the calculations of Kelvin, and he even went so far as to revise the *Origin* in order to bring it in line with the reckonings of the physicists. This attack was easily the weightiest to be brought against the concept of evolution, but Huxley, characteristically, remained imperturbable. Kelvin's charge had originally been lodged against geology, but it was inevitable that it would soon be extended to include biologists who were persuaded of the truth of evolution. Darwin's premises were plainly founded on a time span of "millions of ages" rather than millions of years.

When Kelvin laid the challenge at the door of the biologists in an article published in 1869 in the *Transactions of the Geological Society of Glasgow,* Huxley immediately accepted it and answered in his lecture "Geological Reform." His attempted answer to the charges of the physicists, it must be conceded, was his most unconvincing performance as a defender of Darwin. He utilized all his gifts as a platform artist and did not hesitate to voice his own reservations concerning the value of the mathematics of the physicists. "I desire to point out," he declared, "that this seems to be one of the many cases in which the admitted accuracy of mathematical process is allowed to throw a wholly inadmissible appearance of authority over the results obtained by them. Mathematics may be compared to a mill of exquisite workmanship ... what you get out depends upon what you put in; and as the grandest mill in the world will not extract wheat flour from peascod, so pages of formulae will not get a definite result out of loose data."[28] How far Huxley's rhetoric went in persuading the scientists is, of course, questionable.

But there could be no escaping the contradiction that existed between the findings of biology and physics, and Huxley's failure to offer a reasonable alternative to the argument of Kelvin gives to this essay the sound of special pleading. His work in biology, anatomy, and paleontology had given Huxley an unshakable faith in the truth of evolution. Speaking as a biologist, he washed his hands of all questions of time. "Biology takes her time from geology," he said confidently. "If the geological clock is wrong, all the naturalist will have to do is to modify his notions of the rapidity of change accordingly."

CHAPTER 3

Improving Natural Knowledge

A S a spokesman for science, Huxley in his day succeeded in commanding a hearing that few men have since achieved. The personal qualities, already noted, which he brought to the speaker's platform were, of course, largely responsible for his almost unrivaled popularity as a lecturer; however, he was aided by the fact that the English public at this time was hungry for knowledge—and particularly for that of a scientific nature. The books of Huxley, Darwin, and Lyell—as well as those of such popularizers of science as Hugh Miller and Chambers—enjoyed marked commercial success. Furthermore, it is altogether likely that to serious Victorians the concept of leisure did not have the frivolous connotations it often has today. It was common practice for Englishmen to spend their free time in such uplifting pursuits as reading and lecture-going, and the competition from other entertainment mediums was small for such eminent public teachers as Faraday and Huxley. Today, however, even persons of their unique gifts could not compete successfully against such formidable attractions as television, movies, sporting events, and musical comedies.

Huxley's maiden lecture was delivered at the Royal Institution in April, 1852, when he spoke on "Animal Individuality." The audience that paid its respects to science at the Royal Institution every Friday night in evening dress was drawn primarily from London's upper middle class, and the imperturbable scientist who would coolly squelch the Bishop of Oxford with one deft rhetorical sally some years later was on this occasion quite nervous. "When I took a glimpse into the theatre and saw it full of faces," he recalled, "I did feel most amazingly uncomfortable. I can now quite understand what it is to be going to be hanged and nothing but the necessity of the case prevented me from running away."[1]

In time, however, the young scientist became a favorite speaker at the Royal Institution; and he appeared there with regularity for the next two decades. Another auditorium in which he was a frequent lecturer was the London Institution, where he talked to a middle-class audience somewhat below that of the Royal Institution in social position. Perhaps his favorite audiences, though, were the workingmen for whose special benefit the School of Mines instituted a series of scientific lectures, at which Huxley was a regular speaker. Huxley had a high opinion of the working class as fertile territory in which to scatter the seeds of science. "I want the working classes to understand that science and her ways are great facts for them," he declared in 1855. "I am sick of the dilettante middle class and mean to try what I can do with these hard-handed fellows who live among the facts."[2]

By 1861, Huxley was already moving toward a unique kind of scientific exposition which, with his lecture on the English chalk in 1868, he was to bring to perfection and which was to become one of his trademarks as a speaker. In a lecture in that year on the physical structure of the lobster delivered to a lay audience at the South Kensington Museum,[3] Huxley demonstrated that the principle underlying the anatomy of the sea creature is "unity of plan" and "diversity of execution." The seven successive rings that compose the animal's tail adhere to a plan that is also the underlying organizing principle of the various—more complex—parts of the lobster's body, with the only difference being that the general plan has at different places undergone modification. The ability to discern the common plan in nature offers the man with a clear eye, Huxley says, "a window through which the Infinite may be seen." In later years Huxley, following the example set by Faraday in such lectures as "The Chemical History of a Candle," was to again utilize this approach by taking such unlikely subjects as a piece of chalk, a lump of coal, and a chunk of yeast, and transforming these commonplace objects into scientific "windows" through which the English public could discern the endlessly fascinating and marvelous world of nature.

[56]

I *Lectures to Laymen*

In these lectures Huxley illustrated general principles of science by reference to specific examples: the lump of coal and piece of chalk to explain principles of geologic deposition, the anatomy of the lobster to illustrate principles of evolutionary biology, and the yeast plant to explain such chemical phenomena as fermentation. This singular approach to scientific popularization led Huxley to a lucid presentation of data and ideas that places him at the pinnacle of expository writers in English literature. Part of this success must be attributed to his wealth of subject material: Huxley's extensive acquaintance with the various aspects of nature provided him with an inexhaustible fund of fascinating subjects. And whatever he happened to be interested in at the moment was very likely to find itself the subject of a platform address or a magazine contribution.

The chalk which constitutes so much of the land mass of England has a double-pronged durability. It has, on the one hand, to withstand the steady pounding of the seas; but it has also successfully withstood an onslaught of quite another kind—the lyricism of the poets who have so often taken the impressive physical characteristics of England as the subject of their compositions. It is a well-known fact that Huxley and his science-minded brethren much preferred the poetry of Tennyson to the often bleak and generally unscientific writings of Matthew Arnold. But there was no denying that the cliffs of Dover had inspired Arnold to write one of the finest poems of the Victorian Age—"Dover Beach."

In 1868, Huxley's lecture showed that the chalk could serve science as well as literature as a subject. "On a Piece of Chalk,"[4] the essay often cited as perhaps the most successful attempt to elucidate a complex subject for an audience of laymen, was delivered by Huxley on an overcast day in August, 1868, to the Workingmen's Association in Norwich. Such an imaginative handling of scientific data could only have been written in an age when scientists were accustomed to greater flexibility of style in the presentation of their ideas than they generally have today. Carefully conceived and artfully written, the lecture proves that Huxley not only enjoyed addressing artisans, he spared no effort in preparation and "studiously avoided," as he once declared, "the impertinence of talking *down* to them."[5] "A Piece of Chalk" might just as easily have been delivered before the Royal Society, the British Association, or some other professional body without insulting the education or intelligence of the learned members.

Huxley, the scientist, invests the chalk with a significance heretofore unsuspected by laymen; Huxley, the essayist, describes and explains in terms that rival any piece of fiction for interest, suspense, and enchantment. "What," he asks, "is this wide-spread component of the surface of the earth? and whence did it come?" Before he is finished, he not only advances a history of the chalk and what it is; he also describes and explains many of the fundamental assumptions on which physical science bases its work: "The language of the chalk is not hard to learn, not nearly so hard as Latin, if you only want to get at the broad features of the story it has to tell; and I propose that we now set to work to spell that story out together.[6]

The chalk—or to give it its scientific name, "carbonate of lime" —constitutes so much of England's land mass that to it she "owes her name Albion." Englishmen, of course, have been accustomed to admiring this characteristic of their native landscape for centuries; and it is common knowledge that the mere sight of the magnificent chalky cliffs viewed from the sea is capable of arousing strong feelings of patriotism in a true-born Englishman. It must, therefore, be a surprise to Englishmen who study geology that the chalk is not peculiar to England and is a widely spread substance which underlies a large oval-shaped portion of the globe which includes such distant locations as France, Denmark, Syria, and North Africa. And even more surprising is the story concerning the formation of this mighty edifice. The chalk, Huxley explains, is a vast accumulation of the calcerous skeletons of countless tiny sea creatures, deposited at a time when England was under water.

Huxley then proceeds to support his contention that the chalk is the mud bottom of an ancient sea, and the evidence points to the fact that the sea existed for a long period of time. Although science had not advanced sufficiently to discover the precise date, the epoch was indeed a remote one. For, since the sea evaporated, layers of topsoil have been laid down, and "that dry land, with the bones and teeth of generations of long-lived elephants, hidden away among the gnarled roots and dry leaves of its ancient trees, sank gradually to the bottom of the icy sea, which covered it with huge masses of drift and boulder clay." And it was only subsequent to the second inundation that the water again retreated leaving the land which today is England.

In Huxley's hands a piece of chalk was, therefore, invested with undreamed-of significance. In 1870, in a lecture delivered to the Philosophical Institute at Bindford,[7] a lump of coal assumed mighty proportions. What is necessary is to analyze the object in question in minute detail, for only then are the secrets of the universe unlocked. As Huxley had done when he revealed that the English chalk was made up of thousands of minute chambers, he placed a lump of coal under microscopic analysis. Coal is made up of coin-shaped bodies or sacs which are the spores of certain mosslike plants (lepidendrons). This structure offers the scientist his first clue to its composition. Huxley then describes the complex formation of the mineral—how the beds of seeds were laid, depressed, combined with other sediments, and finally transformed into coal. Scientists at this time were only beginning to understand such processes as coal formation; and, by bringing this information to a lay audience, Huxley was bridging the gulf between the frontiers of science and the public of intelligent laymen.

And what is the moral that the citizen of the nineteenth or twentieth century takes away from this lesson?

Nature is never in a hurry, and seems to have had always before her eyes the adage, keep a thing long enough, and you will find a use for it. She has kept her beds of coal many millions of years without being able to find much use for them; she has sent them down beneath the sea, and the sea-beasts could make nothing of them; she has raised them up into dry land, and laid the black veins bare, and still, for ages and ages, there was no living thing on the face of the earth that could see any sort of value in them; and it was only the other day, so to speak, that she turned a new creature out of her workshop, who by degrees acquired sufficient wits to make a fire, and then to discover that the black rock would burn.[8]

No matter how wanton and extravagant Nature may seem in her processes, she never operates without an end in view. Huxley pictures her as being as meticulous in her accounts as any bookkeeper. For, even when the coal has been burned, providing heat and light, it also releases quantities "of carbonic acid, water, ammonia, and mineral matters exactly equal in weight to the coal."

During the early 1870's, Huxley delivered other lectures to a broad cross-section of the English public on the discoveries of science—to workingmen, students, laymen and fellow scientists. Lectures such as "Biogenesis and Abiogenesis" (1870), "Yeast" (1871), and "The Border Territory Between Plants and Animals" (1876) are typical of these efforts to make science comprehensible to laymen.

"Biogenesis and Abiogenesis" is based on an important discovery made possible by the many recent refinements in the microscope. In 1864, Louis Pasteur, after a series of complicated experiments, had been able to declare with certainty that the air is filled with invisible organisms and that, appearances to the contrary, life is not spontaneously generated. Directly afterward, acting on these discoveries, Lord Lister had revolutionized surgical practice by using carbolic acid as an antiseptic to prevent infection. Huxley's lecture is an explanation of these findings and of their significance.

In "Yeast" Huxley discusses the peculiar properties of the yeast plant which has made it an object of particular interest to chemists for centuries. Utilizing an approach similar to that of the "Chalk" and "Coal" lectures, he surveys the work done by such eminent researchers as Lavoisier, Pasteur, and Robert Boyle in their efforts to analyze the properties of the plant. "The Border Territory Between Plants and Animals" is an attempt to explain a question that had also perplexed scientists for centuries: How can animals be distinguished from plants? The lecture deals largely with two properties peculiar to living things—contractility and photosynthesis.

II Science and Philosophy

In two key essays delivered during the late 1860's Huxley was laying the groundwork for the articles he was to write during the 1870's analyzing the impact of science upon philosophy. These essays were "On the Advisableness of Improving Natural

Knowledge" (1866)[9] and "On the Physical Basis of Life" (1868).[10] The former essay offers solid proof that by 1866 Huxley was already a formidable thinker, as well as a writer of forceful English. A paean to the rise of science, as well as a forthright attack on supernaturalism in its more noxious and thought-retarding manifestations, this discourse was delivered first as a lecture and was subsequently published in the *Fortnightly Review*. The phrase from which the title of the essay is derived was taken from the original prospectus of the Royal Society.

Huxley attempts in this 1866 lecture to date the rise of scientific thinking in England—an entirely new way of looking upon natural phenomena—as having begun with the establishment of the Royal Society in 1645. Huxley never failed to emphasize the importance of the general acceptance of the scientific viewpoint, a subject he frequently returned to in later years. "The period of the Renascence," as he said fourteen years later, "is commonly called that of the 'Revival of Letters'. . . . I think it is very commonly forgotten that the revival of science, effected by the same agency, though less conspicuous, was not less momentous."[11]

In the essay he declares that the approach to life, as exhibited by men of the modern world and by those who lived prior to the dawn of science, is distinctly different. When faced with a catastrophe, for example, it had once been the practice of men to attribute its appearance to divine wrath; and their first thought was invariably to propitiate the gods. Huxley offers two examples from the history of England: the plague which made its appearance in the latter months of 1664, and the great fire which ravaged London in 1666. The distinguishing characteristic is the varying reactions to each of these calamities. Primitive men customarily considered the visitation of a plague as beyond human control and as the direct result of the agency of God. The origins of fire, however, were not so mysterious; and the general belief of mid-seventeenth-century Londoners was that it had been the handiwork of either Republicans or Roman Catholics. The plague in fact had not been the work of a wrathful deity, nor had the fire been set by disappointed members of any political or religious sect. But it was not the habit of men before the birth of science to regard themselves as the authors of their misfortune.

[61]

Significantly, the most important development in the history of science had already taken place by the mid-1660's: the establishment of the Royal Society at Oxford. But some twenty years earlier the spirit of the Society—which for so long was to be the focal point of scientific activity in England, which was to effect so many important changes in English life and thought, and whose growth and development had no parallel in modern history—had as yet not permeated English life. In fact, it was to be many years before its influence actually succeeded in making itself felt.

The questions that Huxley sets out to answer in the essay on "Natural Knowledge" have implications for the twentieth century as well: beyond the fact that science has been able to improve the material circumstances of mankind substantially, what has it accomplished? Moreover, is this contribution the only one which science has been able to make to man? Huxley answers that science has done nothing less than lay the foundation for a new system of ethics and morality: besides conferring "practical benefits on men ... [science] has effected a revolution in their conceptions of the universe and themselves, and has profoundly altered their modes of thinking and their views of right and wrong." Those who were maintaining that science could do nothing more than facilitate technology and satisfy nothing more than man's materialistic cravings could hardly have been given a blunter or more direct rebuttal than this.

Some years later Huxley stated in "Prologue" to *Controverted Questions* that he could see no reason for dividing phenomena into natural and supernatural compartments. All occurrences could be explained in natural terms so long as men had all the data. The less men knew about nature, the more they tended to ascribe things to supernatural causes. "Uncultured man," according to Huxley, "has always taken himself as the standard of comparison, as the center and measure of the world." The savage, therefore, sees in every storm the hand of a wrathful deity; the meteorologist, on the other hand, attributes it to conditions of the atmosphere. So, according to Huxley, as man began accumulating more knowledge of the universe about him, his attitude began to alter; and the fear of former days began to lift as knowledge steadily pushed the frontier of supernaturalism farther and farther away. The foundations of natural knowledge were actually laid "when the savage first learned that the fingers of one hand are fewer than those of both; that it is shorter to cross a stream than to head it; that a stone stops where it is unless it be moved, and that it drops from the hand which lets it go; that light and heat come and go with the sun; that sticks burn away in a fire. . . ."

Huxley's belief in the supremacy of man's reason and intelligence remained a cardinal article of his faith throughout his life, and it sets him apart from many of his contemporaries. Granting that what man knows of the universe and of himself is but a mere fraction of all that can be known, Huxley did not concede anything as "unknowable." Many felt the pursuit of universal knowledge was in effect striving for omnipotence; they saw it as nothing more than a movement whereby man was now aspiring for the place occupied by God. Huxley's old idol Carlyle was one of many nineteenth-century thinkers who saw the rise of science as self-defeating. And even such scientifically inclined Victorians as, for example, Tennyson and Hardy maintained reservations about making total knowledge an ideal. Nowhere have the misgivings of the age been so poignantly recorded as in Hardy's poems "The Oxen" and "God's Funeral."

The ramifications of the rise of knowledge have been farreaching, and that the movement for which Huxley was the most articulate of spokesmen has tremendous, often unquestioning, support in the twentieth century is beyond argument. When C. P. Snow declared that men of science have "the future in their bones," he was giving assent to similar propositions outlined by Huxley. Huxley did not feel so much that he was articulating a new view as restating an old one—one to which men since the dawn of reason had consciously or unconsciously acquiesced—that the foundations of natural knowledge had been laid "when the reason of man came face to face with the facts of nature." And at this point man ceased to be guided solely by instinct and emotion. He discovered that intelligence would be a decisive factor in the struggle for survival; and, once having given assent to this proposition, it would be foolish and inconsistent to place arbitrary limitations upon it. Huxley's view, indeed, is that reason has best served man since his beginnings and that it should be the faculty given priority in the future.

If Huxley's argument has an obvious shortcoming, it is the failure to recognize that man is not exclusively a brain—that his emotions, instincts, and unique anatomy have also played a major role in his history. Other thinkers thought that man's blind, perhaps naïve, faith in the unknown should not be thrust so rudely aside; but Huxley's view was that this day was to arrive eventually, and he took the position that "the sooner, the better." The rise of science had forced upon man a new view of life. For example, man no longer saw himself as the center of the universe but, thanks to astronomers, as an infinitesimal point in the cosmos. And the biologists and anatomists had not supported the venerable notion that man was a unique creature but had found many points at which his anatomy parallels other creatures of the natural world. Many of man's most cherished beliefs, Huxley recognized, were headed for oblivion; and his approach to life must, therefore, be altered. Authority was to be acknowledged only when clearly supported by facts that had been tested by experiment and observation. An active skepticism was a necessary state of mind.

Huxley, it seems, reserved his most controversial efforts for the city of Edinburgh. He had, it is to be recalled, given two lectures on the "Relation of Man to the Lower Animals" at the Philosophic Institute in January, 1862, which caused no small furor. In November, 1868, he was invited by a free-thinking Scottish clergyman, the Reverend James Cranbrook, to give the first of a series of Sunday evening lectures. Huxley used the opportunity to deliver his now famous discourse "On the Physical Basis of Life," which caused such an uproar that a colleague expressed surprise that he had been able to leave Scotland without being stoned.

Huxley, of course, never missed a chance to grind the ax for an unpopular scientific doctrine, and in "On the Physical Basis of Life" he articulates a world view based on the "new morality" which he had so eloquently described in "On Improving Natural Knowledge." Even in his more or less innocent discourse on the English chalk he had demonstrated the necessity of accepting the doctrines of Darwin. "Either each species of crocodile has been specially created," he said at Norwich, "or it has arisen out of some pre-existing form by the operation of natural causes. Choose your hypothesis; I have chosen mine." In enunciating the doctrine of evolution, Huxley had been careful to break down the distinction that separates man from the rest of the animal world. In "The Physical Basis of Life" he goes a step further by destroying the distinctions that separate the animate from the inanimate world. The conclusions toward which "The Physical Basis" point are clearly deterministic in their implications: animate combinations of molecules are subject to the same natural laws that govern inanimate molecular structures. Even those powers generally referred to as the higher faculties cannot be excluded. Man's thoughts, too, Huxley reasons, "are the expressions of molecular changes in the matter of life."

Standing before his audience surrounded by a number of vessels containing such innocent substances as smelling salts, water, and carbonic acid, Huxley dramatically declared that he had before him all the ingredients necessary to produce protoplasm and, therefore, life. "Even those," Huxley writes, "who are aware that matter and life are inseparably connected, may not be prepared for the conclusion plainly suggested by the phrase, 'The Physical Basis of Life.' "[12]

When the ingredients in the vessels which he had before him, Huxley told his audience, are combined in the proper proportions under the proper conditions, they become protoplasm—a substance which exhibits properties unlike those of any one of the constituent elements. One of the properties of protoplasm is "vitality" or what men call "life." The "vitality" of protoplasm is a property just as "aquosity" is a property of water. In the case of the water and the protoplasm, the properties arise as a result of "the nature and the disposition of molecules." Thought and action, therefore, can be traced back ultimately to nothing other than "molecular changes in that matter of life which is the source of our other vital phenomena." Although his language has a distinctly different texture, Huxley in his own way could, when the occasion demanded, be as subtle as Newman. And, just at the point where one expects him to articulate a materialistic philosophy as the one inevitable conclusion to be drawn from his data, Huxley suddenly halts.

Indeed, at this point he emphatically warns against the bland embracing of materialism. "I, individually," he writes, "am no materialist, but, on the contrary, believe materialism to involve grave philosophical error." There would, at first glance, appear to be a gross contradiction here; and Houston Peterson, for one, feels that Huxley has not escaped entangling himself in a paradox. One must inevitably ask: Why, if he is opposed to a materialistic philosophy, has Huxley taken the trouble to saturate the reader with such a materialistic conception of the universe? The answer is that materialistic terminology does not inevitably lead toward an unswerving materialism of viewpoint. Only the superficial or unreflecting fall into this error.[13]

Huxley has presented his argument in materialistic terms because he thought that these are all that man can know of the universe—or, at least, all the reliable evidence gathered so far is of a material nature. But the fact that man's knowledge must be couched in a materialistic terminology does not limit him to accepting this knowledge as the only kind. Huxley's basic premises are really very modest and quite simple. Men are, first, capable of understanding phenomena—that is, their conception of matter represents that which it really is; and, second, man has enough knowledge of cause and effect to postulate certain general rules (which he calls "laws"). Those who grant the assumption—and everyone must, at least tacitly—have committed themselves to a view of the world which is materialistic; and from this attitude, Huxley argues, comes the "gradual banishment from all regions of human thought of what we call spirit and spontaneity"—spirit and spontaneity being nothing but euphemisms for acts which have no cause.

Huxley is able to sidestep accepting a materialistic philosophy by sharply limiting the nature of the physical laws which men acknowledge. They are neither all-embracing nor postulated on an idea of necessity: "It is very convenient to indicate that all the conditions of belief have been fulfilled in this case, by calling the statement that unsupported stones will fall to the ground, 'a law of Nature.' But when, as commonly happens, we change *will* into *must*, we introduce an idea of necessity which most assuredly does not lie in the observed facts, and has no warranty that I can discover elsewhere."[14]

In order to postulate an ironclad philosophy of materialism, one would have to subscribe to an unswerving doctrine of necessity; and such an assumption would have no more justification than most theological doctrines. Thus, Huxley concludes, "the fundamental doctrines of materialism ... and most other 'isms,' lie outside the limits of philosophical inquiry." The only remaining alternative is a skepticism tempered by a philosophical materialism.

This conclusion, needless to say, was not an easy one for many conservative Victorians to accept; and the uproar caused by "On the Physical Basis of Life" was unmatched by that of any other essay of Huxley's. When the lecture was later published in the *Fortnightly Review*, John Morley, the editor of the periodical, attested to the adverse criticism it aroused. "No article," Morley wrote in his *Recollections* "which has appeared in any periodical for a generation back ... excited so profound a sensation as Huxley's memorable paper 'On the Physical Basis of Life.'" Among Huxley's better known critics was James Hutchinson Stirling, famous for an incisive study of Hegel, who advanced the charge that Huxley had invented the substance "protoplasm" to give some scientific basis to his materialistic philosophy.

In an article, "As Regards Protoplasm," Stirling accused Huxley of trying to "found" a philosophy of materialism. Huxley's reply was appropriately cutting. "The mere statement of facts and views long familiar to me," he wrote with heavy irony, "raised a sort of storm in this country ... by exciting the wrath of unscientific persons ... and by giving rise to quite superfluous explosions on the part of some who should have been better informed." Huxley demonstrated that Dr. Stirling's knowledge of chemistry did not even extend to the point where he could use a microscope. Others whose pet prejudices had been touched by this essay, but whose knowledge of chemistry did not even extend to the point where they could deny the existence of protoplasm, contented themselves with calling Huxley a "materialist."

It was, of course, inevitable that Huxley's energetic campaign to acquaint the English public with the truths of science would result in criticism and misunderstanding. Huxley was aware that attempts to make complicated technical material plain to laymen were fraught with peril and that there is a temptation to

[67]

distort complicated material in the interests of simplicity. Whereas specialists were in a position to detect error, laymen were not. In his Preface to Volume VIII of his *Collected Essays,* he commented on this aspect of his work: "It must be admitted that the popularization of science, whether by lecture or essay, has its drawbacks. Success in this department has its perils for those who succeed. The 'people who fail' take their revenge ... by ignoring all the rest of a man's work and glibly labelling him a mere popularizer. If the falsehood were not too glaring, they would say the same of Faraday and Helmholtz and Kelvin."[15]

Many famous men have testified to the effect on their lives exercised by Huxley's discourses. The late anatomist, Sir Grafton Elliot Smith, for example, recalled that, as a young man, he was persuaded to study science by reading certain works of Huxley; William Butler Yeats, on the other hand, somewhat petulantly accused Huxley and Tyndall of having deprived him of his faith in God.

CHAPTER 4

A Liberal Educator

IT was universally agreed in the nineteenth century that the English school system was in a sorry condition, and Lytton Strachey described the state of concern in his essay on Dr. Arnold: "Reform was in the air—political, social, religious; there was even a feeling abroad that our great public schools were not quite all that they should be, and that some change or other—no one precisely knew what—but *some* change in the system of their management, was highly desirable."[1]

One of those who undertook the "reform" of which Strachey speaks was Huxley, but in this venture he was not alone. Indeed, one of the more remarkable aspects of the age is that so many of the great Victorians devoted the best part of their days and nights to the problem. Mill, Newman, and Arnold, for example, wrote extensively on the question of education; but none was more involved than Huxley. Indeed, Huxley's contribution as an educator was not only many-sided, but was perhaps the most far-reaching contribution of his career; for many of the reforms he accomplished are still in effect in the twentieth century.

He was, of course, ideally suited by the wide range of his pursuits to comment and prescribe on the matter. His practical acquaintance with English higher education came from his post as Professor of Natural History at the Royal School of Mines; and his familiarity with elementary education came from his having served as an examiner under the Government's Science and Art Department. He was, moreover, an original investigator and had written numerous textbooks and primers for science study; and, though he reflected the scientific point of view, his deep knowledge of languages, literature, and philosophy bespoke an acquaintance with the humanities as well.

The bulk of Huxley's most considered opinions and proposals respecting English education are contained in the lectures "Scientific Education" (1869), which was delivered at a meeting of the Liverpool Philomathic Society; "Universities: Actual and Ideal" (1874), the ceremonial address delivered after being named Lord Rector of the University of Aberdeen; "Address on University Education" (1876), the ceremonial address delivered at the opening of Johns Hopkins University in Maryland; "Technical Education" (1877), delivered to the Workingmen's Institute and Club in London; "Science and Art in Relation to Education" (1882), delivered at the Liverpool Institution; and an address on behalf of the National Association for the Promotion of Technical Education (1887), delivered to a gathering of Manchester businessmen.[2]

I *A Liberal Education and Where to Find It.*

Huxley's best-known essay on education, however, was delivered in 1868 when he was made principal of the South London Workingmen's College; and he used his inaugural address to fire a salvo of criticism at English education. Many of the criticisms and proposals in this address—"A Liberal Education and Where to Find It"—were repeated and developed in his subsequent writings on the subject; but this particular essay is distinguished by a forcefulness of delivery and by a lucid presentation of ideas. Two passages especially—Huxley's description of the man who has received a truly liberal education and a metaphor in which he compares life to a game of chess—have become classics.

The qualities which a liberal education should cultivate, according to Huxley, are chiefly the masculine characteristics—logic, power, and vigor. They are to be tempered, withal, by a "tender conscience" and a distaste for "vileness":

That man, I think, has had a liberal education who has been so trained in youth that his body is the ready servant of his will, and does with ease and pleasure all the work that, as a mechanism, it is capable of; whose intellect is a clear, cold, logic engine, with all its parts of equal strength, and in smooth working order; ready, like a steam engine, to be turned to any kind of work, and spin the gossamers as well as forge the anchors of the mind; whose mind is stored with a knowledge of the great and fundamental truths of Nature and of the laws of her operation; one who, no stunted ascetic, is full of life and fire, but whose passions are trained to come to heel by a vigorous will, the servant of a tender conscience; who has learned to love all beauty, whether of Nature or of art, to hate all vileness, and to respect others as himself.[3]

Chief among Huxley's criticisms of English education was the vagueness of its goals. He saw a tendency among educators to confuse "liberal education" with technical education. The aim of a liberal education should be the "making of men" and should not be allowed to become a "process of manufacturing human tools, wonderfully adroit in the exercise of some human industry but good for nothing else."

According to Huxley, life is similar to a game of chess, with the pieces being "the phenomena of the universe, the rules ... the laws of Nature." Knowledge of the rules of the game has nothing to do with a particular technological discipline, with a knowledge of "dried up" Greek and Latin fables, or with the dogmatic theology which so many clergymen were anxious to include as a permanent part of the school curriculum. It is "the Laws of Nature" with which the student should be occupying himself, "under which name," Huxley writes, "I include not merely things and their forces but men and their ways." A true "liberal education" should be directed toward giving the student a genuine understanding of these laws.

Instruction in morality is no less important than instruction in the more tangible aspects of nature. The great problem in imparting a system of morality, Huxley writes, is to determine that the foundation underlying moral laws is "as well defined as that which underlies every physical law." Giving a man a good education without a solid moral foundation is pointless. And the student should be given to understand that the consequences that follow upon the breaching of a law of morality are as inevitable and no less tangible than those of breaching a physical law.

Respecting Huxley's ideas on morality, many Victorians were essentially in agreement; but they maintained reservations toward Huxley's extreme approach. To deprive men of a belief in God and a supernatural system of rewards and punishments, and yet expect them to maintain their belief in the existence of moral laws was unrealistic. Matthew Arnold, for example, felt conventional morality could only continue to exist with the backing of conventional theology. And William Mallock's well-known abhorrence of Broad Church rationalizing and of godless morality had its source largely in what he termed the absurd belief "that if the cardinal doctrines of religious orthodoxy were discredited . . . these doctrines, in disappearing, would take away with them nothing but themselves alone."[4]

Also included in Huxley's essay was a critical broadside at England's great public schools. Their approach to learning was too haphazard. Would it be asking too much of these institutions to supply knowledge as well as gentlemanly habits? "Up till within a few years back," Huxley writes, "a boy might have passed through any one of the great public schools with the greatest distinction and credit, and might never so much as have heard of one of the subjects I have just mentioned"—subjects such as geography and history, not to mention the physical and social sciences, not included in the curriculum.

II *London School Board*

In 1870, Huxley was initiated into the higher mysteries of the administrative aspect of English education when he was elected to the first London School Board. He had not wanted to run for the post; for by 1870, his laboratory work had fallen off to almost nothing, and administrative duties were already taking up too much of his time.[5] He accepted the nomination with reluctance, persuaded by the knowledge that, if elected, such a position would offer him a great opportunity to put into practice reforms that he had been considering for some time.

People who complain about schools and teachers today—and who take education entirely for granted—are apt to forget that in England a century ago there was no school system at all. Parliament actually took its first step toward financing public education in 1833, when it allocated twenty thousand pounds for the aid of school societies. But not until 1870 did it act decisively to promote compulsory elementary education by passing Forster's Elementary Education Act. Such legislation was, in fact, long overdue; but there were many deficiencies in the bill. Nevertheless, it had the support of many Victorians (Carlyle, Huxley, Dickens, Bulwer-Lytton, and Mill) who felt that universal schooling was of the primary importance and that it could only be guaranteed by a state system.

This bill doubled the government's appropriation to church schools and arranged for the establishment of new schools to be paid for by local taxes and to be governed by locally elected school boards. Parliament had specifically prohibited denominational teaching in board schools; but, since the candidates for many of the local boards were clergymen and since the boards enjoyed virtually complete autonomy in administering schools in their district, it was rumored that attempts were afoot to sidestep this provision of the act. For this reason, many people, Huxley among them, were anxious to set limits to the powers of the local boards.

Huxley's article "The School Boards: What They Can Do and What They May Do"[6] is a series of reflections on "the duties of the members of the school boards and ... the limits of their power." Although he was aware that the members of the boards were very likely to get themselves entangled in various pettifogging questions (the place of theology in state education) and thus overlook larger questions (the introduction in the curriculum of a program of instruction in the physical sciences), the article advocates that more power be given to the boards themselves. The Education Act, Huxley felt, places too much control in the hands of the Minister of Education, who if he wishes, may use his post despotically and thereby make the boards totally subservient to his desires. Further limitations were placed on the autonomy of local boards by the act, which gave grants in aid to schools on conditions that were set forth in the act. Since the act could be amended by Parliament, Huxley felt that this further limited the free functioning of local boards to prescribe measures best suited to local conditions.

Of more lasting interest, however, are Huxley's reflections on the place that ought to be occupied by theology in state-supported institutions. Huxley would have preferred that his views on this question had not been made public prior to the election, since he did not want this issue to assume proportions that would overshadow other less sensational, but no less momentous, questions. Because he did not want his article on the powers of the school boards to influence the outcome of the election, he submitted it

[73]

to the *Contemporary Review* with the stipulation that its publication be withheld until the contest had been decided. But the editor, James Knowles,[7] sent, in the public interest, prior copies to the London newspapers with the result that the article became a kind of electioneering manifesto; the effect was that Huxley ran second of the elected candidates.

Huxley clearly foresaw that for the government to simultaneously award grants-in-aid to schools while sanctioning the dissemination of the beliefs of any one religious group could be the start of a dangerous trend. The Education Act did, in fact, expressly forbid the teaching of "catechisms and formularies" of any distinct religious denomination; but plans were already being laid to sidestep this provision. Representatives of various religious interests (numerous clergymen running for the boards) were talking of permitting the teaching of whatever doctrines the various denominations held in common. Huxley, who strongly opposed any attempt to sidestep the Parliamentary prohibition on religion, called for an interpretation by the boards that would be in keeping with the spirit, as well as the letter, of the act.

Reading of the Bible, however, was a different question. Only by an acquaintance with Holy Writ would it be possible to avoid confounding "the science, morality, with the affection religion." The Bible, moreover, is "a vast residuum of moral beauty and grandeur ... and has been woven into the life of all that is best and noblest in English history." On these grounds Huxley favors making Bible-reading a requirement in the curriculum. As far as the rest of the elementary curriculum is concerned, he recommends physical training; the rudiments of science, singing and domestic science for girls; and drawing, in addition to comprehensive instructions in the subjects which are "the tools of knowledge—reading, writing, and elementary mathematics."

III *Educational Reform*

In a talk on "Scientific Education" delivered in Liverpool in 1869, Huxley advanced a description of the scientific subjects which a solid elementary curriculum should comprise. For a basic course in science he suggests an equivalent of the German *Erdkunde* ("Earth knowledge") which would provide an introduction to science and the answers to many questions about which children are naturally curious. The student would then progress to botany and physics. His reasons for including these sciences are instructive: there are, Huxley felt, two "kinds of physical science: the one regards form and the relation of forms to one another; the other deals with causes and effects. In many of what we term sciences, these two kinds are mixed up together; but systematic botany is a pure example of the former kind, and physics of the latter kind, of science."

Because of the heavy stress that he generally placed on the teaching of science, the belief grew that Huxley favored it almost to the exclusion of all other subjects. It is true that many of the claims Huxley made on behalf of the teaching of science (especially in such early essays as "Natural History as Knowledge, Discipline, and Power") sound somewhat extravagant; but, in the fashion of many articulate advocates, he often overstates his case. However, it should be emphasized that Huxley did not urge science instruction at the expense of the humanities. If there were any men of science who favored such a plan, Huxley was not at one with them. His own writings, abundant in literary and poetic allusions, tacitly bespeak his own breadth of culture.

In the twentieth century, of course, great stress is laid upon the importance of the physical sciences, in many instances to the exclusion of other pursuits. This unhappy state of affairs is a perversion of the kind of education which Huxley visualized, for he was far from being a narrow specialist. He saw the truly educated man as being at home in any discipline, and he was never a spokesman for a superficial educational program. In "Scientific Education" he states his position on the question: "There are other forms of culture besides physical science; and I should be profoundly sorry to see the fact forgotten, or even to observe a tendency to starve, or cripple, literary, or aesthetic, culture for the sake of science. Such a narrow view of the nature of education has nothing to do with my firm conviction that a complete and thorough scientific culture ought to be introduced into all schools."[8]

Englishmen, Huxley felt, should be made aware of the crucial need for science; and it should be given the place in the schools of a major subject, of "the most favored nation." But it was not to be a question of which area of study should predominate. "It is a question," Huxley wrote in "Science and Art in Relation to Education," "of what topics of education you shall select which will combine all the needful elements in such due proportion as to give the greatest amount of food, support, and encouragement to those faculties which enable us to appreciate truth ... and to avoid that which is bad, and coarse, and ugly."[9]

The opposition to the wholesale introduction of science derived in the most part from two directions. Some educators were opposed to it on principle; others based their opposition on practical considerations. The former group consisted mainly of those who felt universities should be training grounds for gentlemen and who were against any radical reforms in primary and secondary education. Others, less traditional, were conscious of costs. The facilities necessary for scientific study were elaborate and nearly always expensive, and the training of qualified instructors presented another obstacle. Huxley was himself acutely aware of the difficulties involved in training teachers in adequate numbers. In June, 1871, he inaugurated a course in general biology for teachers at the South Kensington Museum. He repeated it the following summer with such a success that he introduced it at the School of Mines the following October.[10]

Another area of study which Huxley also stressed was the teaching of foreign languages, particularly French, German, and Latin. Nearly everyone suffers under the limitations of language. "The knowledge," according to Huxley, "of some other language than one's own is ... one of the safest ways of delivering yourself from the bondage of words." Latin in addition offers the key to much of English and all the Romance languages: a knowledge of German and French opens vast new fields in art and science, while affording insight into people who have played a major part in the history of Western civilization.

Huxley could be outspoken in his criticisms of English educational institutions, especially of the great universities of Oxford and Cambridge: "When I think of the host of pleasant, moneyed, well-bred young gentlemen, who do a little learning and much boating by Cam and Isis, the vision is a pleasant one; and, as a patriot, I rejoice that the youth of the upper and richer classes of the nation receive a wholesome and a manly training, however small may be the modicum of knowledge they gather, in the intervals of this, their serious business...."[11]

Huxley, no shallow social reformer, did not wish to deny the privileged classes their leisure activities; but he also knew that a nation's greatest resource was its talented citizens—those who combined extraordinary ability with the determination to use it. England, by denying its most gifted men education and opportunity, would only impair her own well-being. For the student of genius he advocated making accessible the best training possible. Huxley once declared "that if the nation could purchase a potential Watt, or Davy, or Faraday, at the cost of a hundred thousand pounds down, he would be dirt-cheap at the money. It is a mere commonplace and everyday piece of knowledge, that what these three men did has produced untold millions of wealth, in the narrowest economical sense of the word."[12]

England's growing dependence on technology would require more and more people with a familiarity with the principles of science. England's proficiency in this direction had, indeed, made her a world power; and only a continuing proficiency could maintain her position in the face of growing competition from a developing America and a recently united Germany. In a plain-spoken lecture to the businessmen of Manchester in 1887, Huxley clearly described the relationship between scientific education and industry:

Our machinery, our chemical process or dyeworks, and a thousand operations which it is not necessary to mention, are all directly and immediately connected with science. You have to look among your workmen and foremen for persons who shall intelligently grasp the modifications, based upon science, which are constantly being introduced into these industrial processes. I do not mean that you want professional chemists, or physicists, or mathematicians, or the like, but you want people sufficiently familiar with the broad principles which underlie industrial operations to be able to adapt themselves to new conditions.[13]

In the same lecture he also describes the dilemma that faced England at the close of the nineteenth century. The individual wage earner, on the one hand, would have to be provided with a return from his labor that would give him a standard of living not below the "point at which decency and cleanliness and order and habits of morality can reasonably be expected to exist." But the necessity to compete successfully with other industrial nations, while providing such a wage, was of equal importance; and, to Huxley, an improved educational system with emphasis on science was the solution to this dilemma.

Other changes urged by Huxley were of a more general nature. He was in favor of government subsidies for scientific research and for the creation of more posts for scientists. It was plainly with the memory of his own difficulties in finding a post after returning to England in 1850 that he told his audience at Aberdeen: "It is better for a man's worldly prospects to be a drunkard, than to be smitten with the divine dipsomania of the original investigator."

IV *Medical Eduation*

After his graduation from Charing Cross—except for his five years as assistant surgeon on the *Rattlesnake*—Huxley never practiced medicine. However, he maintained a lifelong interest in the profession and served as an examiner at the University of London for more than a decade. He made recommendations concerning medical education in his lecture on "Scientific Education," as well as in his address at Aberdeen and the ceremonial address at Johns Hopkins. By and large, the proposals are similar to recommendations made in a number of lectures devoted exclusively to aspects of the profession—"Medical Education" (1870), "Connection of the Biological Sciences with Medicine" (1881), and "The State and the Medical Profession" (1884).[14]

The cornerstone of Huxley's plan of reforms for medical education was that the medical student, with no more than three or four years to give to his studies, must make maximum use of his time. "Methuselah might, with much propriety," Huxley told the medical students at Aberdeen, "have taken half a century to get his doctor's degree; and might, very fairly, have been required to pass a practical examination in the contents of the British Museum, before commencing practice as a promising young fellow of two hundred, or thereabouts. But you have four years to do your work in, and are turned loose, to save or slay, at two or three and twenty." Huxley thought it the gravest of offenses to waste the time of a medical student with anything not directly relevant to medical practice. Accordingly, he advocated abolishing botany and zoology from the medical curriculum, as well as comparative anatomy, and teaching only "those branches of physics and chemistry which bear directly on physiology."

Time was also wasted in medical schools because so many students arrived with only a superficial knowledge of physical science and with no experience in practical laboratory work. It was, therefore, the job of primary and secondary schools to impart a thorough grounding in botany, zoology, physics, and chemistry for future medical students. Another reform advocated by Huxley was successive rather than simultaneous study of subjects. A doctor should have of the human body, the kind of "practical, familiar, finger-end knowledge," he declared at Aberdeen, "which a watchmaker has of a watch ... and which is to be had not by sharing attention between sundry subjects, but by concentrating your minds, week after week, and month after month, until the greater truths of anatomy and physiology have become an organic part of your minds."

This position of arguing for more concentrated rather than for broader studies was a strange one for Huxley. It did not have its basis, of course, in the belief that doctors should not be men of wide learning. "I hold as strongly as anyone can do," he said at Aberdeen, "that the medical practitioner's right to be a person of education and good general culture; but I also hold by the old theory of a Faculty, that a man should have his general culture before he devotes himself to the special studies of that Faculty." The "general culture," Huxley felt, should be imparted in the primary and secondary schools.

Medical education, like English education generally, also suffered from "the unreality and bookishness of the knowledge taught." It would be better, he felt, if two or three central branches were set up to teach the theoretical aspects of medicine to the students in all the London medical schools. Doing so would establish uniform standards for all and would allow the medical schools to concentrate exclusively on practical instruction in anatomy and physiology.

V Visit to Yankeeland

Huxley served, in all, a total of fourteen months on the London School Board. When he left, it was with the vow to "avoid semi-political work hereafter." But it was not the nature of the post itself which forced his retirement. Dyspepsia, with all its attendant discomforts, returned in December, 1871, and brought all his activities to a halt, including his lectures at the School of Mines. Nevertheless, he had accomplished a great deal during the previous twelve months. The year had in fact been claimed by a variety of activities—administrative, scientific, and literary. During the summer, which was spent with his family at St. Andrews, he managed to write two significant articles, "Mr. Darwin's Critics" and "Administrative Nihilism." Indeed, the very variety of Huxley's pursuits was winning respect for him from many quarters. In a letter to Darwin, Sir Joseph Hooker expressed a thought that must have been in the minds of many others at this time. "When I read Huxley," he confided, "I feel quite infantile in intellect."[15]

In June, 1872, Huxley made the first of his many journeys in search of health. The school had granted him a two-month leave (later extended to three); and, in the company of his wife, he traveled to Egypt. He returned to England the following April, bearded and sunburned but not entirely cured of his malady. Other difficulties followed his decision to move from his old home in Abbey Place—which the family by this time had outgrown— to new quarters at No. 4 Marlborough Place. But the year ended on a happy note: he was notified by Aberdeen University that the institution's students had elected him Lord Rector. And the fact that his dyspepsia had disappeared enabled him to anticipate the coming year with new vigor. Part of the improvement in his health during these years can be attributed to a strict diet. Except for an occasional glass of wine he gave up alcoholic beverages entirely, and cut down considerably on his food intake as well. Another health measure was abandoning cigarettes in favor of cigars in 1873.

One of Huxley's principal worries at this time was money. His trip to Egypt had actually been made possible by a discreet gift of twenty-one hundred pounds raised by a committee of scientists and deposited to his bank account by Darwin. And the cost of his new home had been partly allayed by a generous loan from Tyndall. As a result, Huxley during these years always had looked for any enterprise that would add to his income. Then, as now, teachers and researchers were not among the highest paid members of society; and his letters frequently contain allusions to his difficulties supporting his family. In a letter to a fellow scientist who was contemplating marriage, he writes: "May you have as good a wife and as much a 'happy family' as I have, though I would advise you—the hardness of the times being considered—to be satisfied with fewer than seven members thereof."[16]

It was, therefore, primarily his need for money that started Huxley's thinking about visiting America. Although his historic trip did not take place until 1876, the first mention of it is to be found in a letter to Darwin written in March, 1874: "I have an awfully tempting offer to go to Yankeeland on a lecturing expedition, and I am seriously thinking of making an experiment next spring. The chance of clearing two or three thousand pounds in as many months is not to be sneezed at by a *père de famille.*"[17]

Most of his significant publications between 1873 and 1875 were of a scientific nature—notable exceptions being "The Hypothesis That Animals Are Automata" and "Universities: Actual and Ideal." His most noteworthy publication of 1876, "Address on University Education," was delivered in America in September; for Huxley had made the trip to "Yankeeland" accompanied only by his wife. They had sailed on the *Germanic* a few weeks after their twenty-first wedding anniversary and they regarded the trip as a second honeymoon.

The trip was not only a significant personal occasion, but also a professional satisfaction, for the reception he received in America left no doubt of the great impact his writings had made in the New World. "The whole nation is electrified at the news that Professor Huxley is going to visit us next fall," one of Huxley's American admirers wrote. "We will make infinitely more of him than we did of the Prince of Wales and his retinue of lords and dukes."[18] The prophecy proved to be largely correct.

Huxley's itinerary called for him to spend the first few days of his stay in New York. On deck as his ship entered New York Harbor, Huxley registered a favorable first impression of America. Describing the buildings of the Western Union Telegraph Company and the New York *Tribune,* then the two tallest structures on the city's skyline, he remarked: "Ah, that is interesting; that is American. In the Old World the first thing you see as you approach a great city are steeples; here you see, first, centers of intelligence."[19]

After New York, Huxley spent a strenuous week in New Haven as the guest of Professor O. C. Marsh, the great paleontologist who was at that time in residence at Yale University. Marsh's researches in the American West had uncovered all kinds of new fossils, one of which was a complete genealogy of the horse. Since he intended to lecture in New York on the horse, Huxley was quite anxious to see Marsh's fossil collection, and for his part, Marsh was only too ready to oblige. The result was that Huxley substantially altered his New York address on the basis of Marsh's specimens. "With the generosity of true greatness," Marsh later wrote, "he gave up his own opinions in the face of new truth, and took my conclusions as the basis of his famous New York lecture on the horse."[20] Huxley and Marsh— two very fiery characters—seem to have gotten on famously. In a letter to his wife Huxley described his host as "a wonderfully good fellow, full of fun and stories about his Western adventures, and the collection of fossils are the most wonderful thing I ever saw."[21]

The "Lectures on Evolution"[22] were delivered in New York on September 18, 20, and 22. These three lectures, closely reasoned fruits of fifteen years of writing and reflecting on the subject, are a balanced combination of scientific exposition and lucid statement; and they constitute, along with *Man's Place in Nature,* the best of Huxley's popular expositions of evolution. That he went to such pains on behalf of an American audience is testimony of his high respect for the New World and for the major role he felt it would play in the future of science. The first two lectures represent an attempt to illustrate the various hypotheses that have been advanced respecting the history of nature, and the third evaluates the evidence on which evolutionary doctrine rests its case.

The title of the first lecture is "Three Hypotheses Respecting the History of Nature." These three hypotheses are the accounts of creation which had wide support at that time. They are, first, that the world in a form similar to its present state has always existed; second, that it came into being suddenly in a manner like that described in the seventh book of *Paradise Lost;* third, that the world arrived at its present form gradually, through process of evolution. Although Huxley's reputation had preceded him, and probably no one was unaware of the hypothesis behind which he stood, he gives a comprehensive account of each.

Evidence points away from the likelihood that nature has always existed in its present state. The paleontological record, especially, clearly exhibits that the plants and animals of the present time have been only of temporary duration and were preceded by a different natural state. The second hypothesis—which Huxley chooses to call "the Miltonic" rather than "the Biblical" because it is stated most clearly in Milton's great poem and because he did not wish to give offense unnecessarily—is also found to be contrary to paleontological evidence respecting the order of appearance of different forms of life. Following the Bible, Milton has aquatic birds and animals appearing simultaneously—on the fifth day; and plant life had appeared on the third day. Since all life originated in the sea, this order of creation was plainly in error. Birds, moreover, appeared well after fishes, not simultaneously with them. Milton's gloss on Genesis, whatever its value as poetry, can hardly be considered as a literal account of the beginnings of life.

In the second lecture, Huxley discusses geological and paleontological evidence bearing on the third hypothesis—evolution. He discredits the concept that any given form of life *must* vary, and he makes the connection between variation and environment. Certain types of animal life have persisted, but this fact doesn't mean that others have not evolved. Huxley offers Cuvier as an example of a great scientist who, having investigated the possibility of evolution, concluded that it hadn't occurred. Cuvier's error was that he failed to recognize that life does not evolve necessarily, but only when modifications in an environment favor such change. This, Huxley writes, was the great contribution of Darwin: he had established the connection between the two most important factors in the evolutionary process.

Favorable paleontological deposits have made it possible to trace the evolution of many of the present members of the equine family. For this reason, the horse is a classic subject for the demonstration of evolution in action. Moreover, the animal itself is the best example of how the process produces a creature of unparalleled precision and beauty: "The horse is in many ways a remarkable animal; not least so in the fact that it presents us with an example of one of the most perfect pieces of machinery in the living world. In truth, among the works of human ingenuity it cannot be said that there is any locomotive so perfectly adapted to its purpose doing so much work with so small a quantity of fuel, as this machine of nature's manufacture—the horse."[23]

The horse is also an apt illustration in this instance because its fossil deposits of North America have yielded the best succession of forms. But evolution in 1876 had to be regarded as still a theory, not as a proven fact; and on this note Huxley concludes. The logical basis of the theory is "the coincidence of the observed facts with theoretical requirements." For those unconvinced by the fossil record or unhappy with the idea that life changed with the passage of time, Huxley offers a choice no less palatable: "The only escape, if it be a way of escape, from the conclusions which I have indicated, is the supposition that all the equine forms have been created separately at separate epochs of time."

The following day Huxley left America. By and large, Huxley was impressed by the similarities between the two countries, although he felt America was twenty years behind England in freedom of thought. Unlike Arnold, Wilde, Dickens, and so many other eminent Victorians who registered unfavorable impressions of America, Huxley had been quite pleased by what he saw. "I had a very pleasant trip in Yankeeland," he wrote to a colleague, "and did *not* give utterance to a good deal that I am reported to have said there."[24] He was more amused than irritated by the distorted versions of himself and his ideas that had appeared in the American press.

Back in England, Huxley resumed his work. In 1877 he published three books: *American Addresses, Anatomy of Invertebrate Animals,* and *Physiography.* The last book, subtitled *"An Introduction to the Study of Nature,"* had its source in a series of lectures eight years before for young people at the London Institute and sold 3,386 copies in the first six weeks after publication. Huxley later revised it three times, and it eventually became one of the most influential and revolutionary textbooks of the century in Europe as well as in England. The book dealt with the fundamental principles of chemistry, physics, and geology; and it conveyed scientific concepts by proceeding from facts and ideas already well-known to the student. For example, principles of geology were illustrated by concrete examples to be found in the basin of the Thames. Notable for its simplicity and charm of style, only Huxley could have written it.

By and large, these were years of extraordinary activity and triumph. The skepticism with which people had been used to regarding evolutionists began to disappear. The fact that Darwin's alma mater, Cambridge, had in 1877 seen fit to confer an honorary degree upon Darwin was a sign that the times were beginning to alter. And, when he died five years later, he was buried in Westminster Abbey. In 1879 Huxley, too, received an honorary degree from Cambridge. The evolutionary party was suddenly engulfed in unaccustomed respectability.

These were, however, just some of the many signs that the wheel had come full circle and that the evolutionists were now spokesmen for the new orthodoxy. Huxley marked the twentieth birthday of the *Origin* with a talk at the Royal Institution, "On the Coming of Age of the Origin of Species"—the talk in which he made his wry comments on "our contemporaries of twenty years before." The reference, of course, was to Wilberforce and Owen, both of whom were by this time thoroughgoing anachronisms. Owen, once the possessor of an enormous reputation, was now living the life of a recluse; alone except for the cats he kept in his household, he was all but forgotten. At the time of his death in 1892, a delegation of fellow scientists was to have a difficult time raising money for a suitable memorial.

VI *Controversy with Arnold*

On October 1, 1880, Huxley delivered the address at the formal opening of the Josiah Mason College in Birmingham. Mason, a hardheaded, self-educated businessman, had ordered in the charter of the college which he was founding the exclusion

from the curriculum of "mere literary instruction and education"—by which he meant only the prohibition of instruction in
Classical languages. The aim of the school was to place heavy
emphasis on the teaching of practical and theoretical science,
but the curriculum was also to include instruction in English,
as well as in modern foreign languages. Huxley took the occasion
to deliver a ringing ultimatum to the "levites in charge of the
ark of culture"—in other words, the Classicists.

This speech is the most militant, outspoken, and at times even
strident essay in Huxley's campaign to deprive the Classics of
the high place they held in university education. Moreover, Huxley refers to Matthew Arnold in such a way—calling him at one
point "our chief apostle of culture"—as to associate him with a
narrow, superficial humanism. The remark made a reply by
Arnold unavoidable, and he duly replied in "Literature and Science," delivered in America in 1883.

In "Science and Culture" Huxley describes opposition to introduction of the physical sciences into education as coming
mainly from two sources: businessmen, "who pride themselves
as being the representatives of practicality," and Classical schol-
ars, who regard themselves as "monopolists of liberal education."
Both views, he says, are incorrect. The business community is
dependent upon the diffusion of scientific education as an "abso-
lutely essential condition for industrial progress." And the Classicists are mistaken in their belief that "the study of physical science is incompetent to confer culture." For the purpose of at-
taining real culture, Huxley says, "an exclusively scientific education is at least as effectual as an exclusively literary education."
And, while he agrees with Arnold's statement that criticism of
life is the essence of culture, he takes issue with Arnold on his
belief "that literature contains the materials which suffice for the
construction of such a criticism." According to Huxley, the most
necessary ingredient is knowledge of the physical sciences. The
rapid accumulation of knowledge in all areas of physical sciences
during the nineteenth century, a development apparent to anyone with even a passing acquaintance with them, makes this
conclusion of Huxley's hardly a startling one.

Fortunately, Huxley's slighting remarks about Arnold did not
lead to a rough-and-tumble controversy in which the personal-

ities of the two men overshadowed the questions involved. Each, by anybody's estimate, must figure among the greatest Englishmen of his century; and a controversial battle conducted along the lines of Huxley's warfare with Gladstone would not have redounded to the credit of either.

Arnold wisely waited before replying. He was obviously anxious in his rejoinder, "Literature and Science," to stress the points with which he agreed with Huxley. Arnold was aware that Huxley was a master of in-fighting when the occasion demanded it, and he also knew that in such an exchange, whatever the merits of his own argument, he was very likely to come out second best. "The ability and pugnacity of the partisans of natural science make them formidable persons to contradict,"[25] he remarks wryly. "Literature and Science" is, therefore, a carefully reasoned, intelligent analysis of the relative value of scientific and literary education; and it compares favorably to Huxley's "Science and Culture." Arnold pushed the emphasis of education back to man himself; Huxley had laid stress on man understanding the world rather than himself. Unquestionably, there is something to be said for each approach.

Arnold addresses himself to the question whether the "movement for ousting letters from their old predominance in education . . . ought to prevail." He cautions against confusing the study of *belles-lettres* with "a superficial humanism, the opposite of science or true knowledge." Because of the zeal of reformers to gain a place for science in the curriculum, they were not above referring with disdain to the study of letters. Huxley, for example, brushed aside the study of the ancients as "dried up Greek and Latin fables" and referred to modern literature as "the caterwauling of poets."

Arnold placed his finger directly on the weakness of the argument of the reformers: they were chiefly occupied in stressing practicality. Arnold had no bias against utility in his concept of education, but, he wrote, "those who are giving to natural knowledge the chief place in the education . . . leave one important thing out of their account: the constitution of human nature." This argument is most tellingly brought to bear against many of the views of Huxley. In his education essays he was constantly stressing the development of "clear, cold logic engines"; and his views of religion are often criticized for the naïve belief that the Bible could retain its authority as a moral lawgiver even if people did not believe that it was directly inspired by God. According to Arnold, there is in man a desire to relate knowledge of a factual nature to conduct and to beauty. And this Huxley's study of science neither does nor pretends to do.

Arnold was also against comparisons that attempted to measure the relative merits of the study of the humanities and the sciences, for he recognized that knowledge does not permit of such easy compartmentalization. But as a practical word for those who found themselves unable to choose between the study of humane letters, and of the natural sciences, Arnold wrote: "The great majority of mankind, all who have not exceptional aptitudes, for the study of nature, would do well, I cannot but think, to choose to be educated in humane letters rather than in the natural sciences. Letters will call out their being at more points, will make them live more."[26]

Neither Huxley nor Arnold pretended to be able to advise any individual as to how or where he should direct his studies. Each felt, however, in the last analysis, that the majority of men would do best to follow the direction he himself had gone. Huxley thought mankind would profit most by an understanding of the world around him; Arnold thought it was most profitable for man to understand himself.

There is no question that Huxley was hard at work on a campaign to de-emphasize the Classics as the mainstay of university education. The irony is, however, that Huxley himself would be shocked to learn of the very small place they enjoy today in university education. For himself, he felt that the Classics had less relevance to modern life than did the literary tradition which had its roots in the Renaissance and which, in combination with the discoveries of science, was providing the basis for what he called the "new morality." But he did not underestimate the ancients; he had a high opinion of their sagacity, a fact attested to by his undertaking the study of Greek in middle life.

Although Arnold and Huxley held many differing views, this public disagreement might easily have been avoided. Their acquaintance, after all, went back to the year 1868, when Huxley had extended an invitation to Arnold to attend the annual dinner of the Geological Society. If Huxley's bias in favor of the sciences separated him from Arnold's equally strong bias in favor of the humanities, the exchange demonstrated that at many points they shared common ground. What emerged from this much publicized exchange of views was that Huxley's keen advocacy of the physical sciences did not blind him to the importance of literary education, and that Arnold's favoring of letters did not mean that he was opposed to the introduction of science in school and university curriculum.

CHAPTER 5

Metaphysics

H UXLEY was a charter member of the "once famous" (now legendary) Metaphysical Society, and it is probably more than coincidence that his own writings on philosophical subjects coincided almost exactly with the years of the society's existence. Even Huxley, accustomed as he was to the company of such profound thinkers as Herbert Spencer, Darwin, and Tyndall, must have derived tremendous stimulation from association with such a divergent group as the society provided. The society, the brainchild of James Knowles, held its first meeting in April, 1869; endured for eleven years; and boasted the membership of just about every Victorian with any claim to intellectual eminence with only three exceptions—Newman, Mill, and Spencer, each of whom declined membership. Among the members were John Ruskin, Lord Tennyson, William Gladstone, Walter Bagehot, R. H. Hutton, James Froude, and Archbishop Manning; and the necessity to counter the arguments of such an articulate and varied group doubtless brought Huxley to grips with problems that might otherwise have remained in an unformed state.

It was the regular practice of members to contribute papers, and the titles of those read by Huxley convey the general drift of their contents. His first contribution, "Hume, Kant, and Whately on the Immortality of the Soul," attempts to show that moral faith or revelation, rather than logic, is the only grounds for a belief in immortality.[1] In his second, "Has a Frog a Soul?" he bases an argument against immortality on the facts of physiology; in his third, "Evidence of the Miracle of the Resurrection," he advances a demonstration that evidence of Christ's resurrection from death is scientifically unverifiable and belief in it must rest on faith. The presence of such articulate spokesmen for orthodoxy as Wilfred Ward and Gladstone forced Huxley in these short papers to be more heavily ironic and critical of Christianity than was his custom. His paper on the "Resurrection" moved Newman, who had declined membership because he did not wish to associate with free thinkers, to thank his "stars" that he did not have to witness such blasphemy.

Huxley is remembered by other members as having been one of the most outspoken and active of the society's members. One colleague, James Hinton, was so impressed by Huxley's genius for dialectics that he confided the thought that Huxley had made a mistake in devoting his life to science since "the true bent of his genius is to metaphysics."[2] What contemporaries such as Hinton probably did not know, however, was that metaphysics had been a lifelong concern of Huxley's. A congenital sufferer from the discomforts of insomnia, he had been accustomed to reading himself to sleep with metaphysical works for many years. He had made an early acquaintance—while still in his early teen years—with such deep thinkers as William Hamilton (who at that time was enjoying something of a vogue) and David Hume. Indeed, Huxley's familiarity with the thought of Hume was such that when, in 1878, he was asked by John Morley to contribute a volume on the Scotch philosopher to the "English Men of Letters Series," he was able to write it within the incredibly short space of six weeks.

Other interests, however, had conspired to prevent Huxley from writing on philosophical subjects before 1870. Perhaps his first attempt to comprehensively treat an abstract question was "On the Physical Basis of Life," in which he had attempted to articulate a philosophical approach with distinctly scientific foundations to natural phenomena. He addressed himself to another metaphysical problem two years later in a lecture on Descartes, and the following year (1871) he contributed an article on Bishop Berkeley to *Macmillan's Magazine*. In 1874 he expanded some of the ideas that he had treated in his Lecture on Descartes in a lecture given at the Cambridge YMCA on "Animal Automata." The Hume book appeared in 1878, and the following year he contributed another article on Bishop Berkeley to the *Nineteenth Century*. The Metaphysical Society died in 1880 ("of too much love," Huxley remarked); and, when Huxley once again returned to abstract problems after his retirement from the School of Mines in 1884, he devoted himself chiefly to theological rather than metaphysical questions.

I *Correspondence with Kingsley*

In writing on theology and philosophy, it was Huxley's practice to approach the subject impersonally rather than autobiographically. In the Hume volume Huxley wrote "that philosophy lies in the province of science, and not in that of letters";[3] and he accordingly examined abstract questions with the objectivity that he conducted experiments in the laboratory. Huxley shared Carlyle's belief that the personal doubts, spiritual crises, and moral questionings of an individual are unfit matters for public discussion; and his one excursion into autobiography ("Autobiography") was a reluctant one and only written because he wished to avoid the misrepresentation that would follow had someone else done the job. Huxley loved and respected truth, but he knew that autobiography was seldom anything more than superior fiction. Since he was naturally reticent about his personal life, he never succumbed to the vogue to produce copy by self-dramatization, even though the bookstalls of the time were filled with works written after the fashion of the *Confessions* of Rousseau—Froude's *Nemesis of Faith,* Mill's *Autobiography,* and Leslie Stephen's *An Agnostic's Apology,* as well as with similar works by lesser men. Though Huxley recognized the merit of these works, he felt that they exhibited a deplorable lack of taste and a weakness of character.

This reticence marks not only his public utterances but his private correspondence as well. Save for an occasional *cri de coeur,* Huxley seldom writes frankly and without reservation about his own personal feelings. One striking exception, however, was a long letter written in 1860, shortly after the sudden death of his son Noel from scarlet fever, to the Reverend Charles Kingsley. Huxley's wife at the time was in a state of collapse, and he himself was suffering from a severe mental depression. This letter of Huxley's, a revealing justification of his own philosophical skepticism (his refusal, as he says, "to put faith in that which does not rest upon sufficient evidence"),[4] was written in response to an earlier letter of condolence from Kingsley (now lost) in which the clergyman had suggested that the only consolation for such grief was a belief in the Christian doctrine of immortality.

In his reply Huxley acknowledges the truth in Kingsley's claim—that the doctrine offers enormous consolation for afflicted persons—but he does not see how he can embrace it without sacrificing his fidelity to truth. "Had I lived a couple of centuries earlier," he writes, referring to the hours of his deepest grief, "I could have fancied a devil scoffing at me ... and asking me what profit it was to have stripped myself of the hopes and consolations of the mass of mankind?"5 Huxley's reply is that a fidelity to truth is of greater value than any amount of consolation or wealth—that "truth is greater than much profit ... and if wife and child and name and fame were all lost to me one after the other as the penalty, still I will not lie." Had Huxley been given to self-dramatization, such a passage as this one might be considered as mere rhetoric; however, it stands almost alone in Huxley's correspondence, and there is good reason to feel that it is an accurate and literal statement of his personal feelings.

An individual's worth, Huxley feels, depends, first, on the quality of the ideals which can be said to guide his life; and second, on the amount of success he has had in fulfilling those ideals. "The longer I live," he declares, "the more obvious it is to me that the most sacred act of a man's life is to say and to feel, I believe such to be true. All the greatest rewards and all the heaviest penalties of existence cling about that act."

He declares that he will only accept as true those doctrines which rest on sufficient evidence; and, so far as theological doctrines are concerned, they must be subjected to the same verification as those by which the great generalizations of science are tested. "I know what I mean," he writes in his letter, "when I say I believe in the law of the inverse squares, and I will not rest my life and my hopes upon weaker convictions.... Measured by this standard," he asks Kingsley, "what becomes of the doctrine of immortality?"

Although the conclusions suggested by science often point away from theological teachings, there are nevertheless many points of analogy; and by the nature of their vocations the scientist (Huxley) in many respects resembles the man of the cloth

(Kingsley): "Science seems to me to teach in the highest and strongest manner the great truth which is embodied in the Christian conception of entire surrender to the will of God. Sit down before a fact as a little child, be prepared to give up every preconceived notion, follow humbly wherever and to whatever abysses nature leads, or you shall learn nothing. I have only begun to learn content and peace of mind since I have resolved at all risks to do this."[6]

Huxley felt that the tendency to associate theology, religion, and morality had had an enormously mischievous effect on modern thinking; moreover, the modern tendency to lump them together and use the terms almost interchangeably had given rise to a general misconception concerning the nature of the terms. Religion and theology, Huxley felt, were entirely distinct from one another. Carlyle's *"Sartor Resartus,"* he writes to Kingsley, "led me to know that a deep sense of religion was compatible with the entire absence of theology." Virtue was its own reward, and the nature of morality had a practical basis. Religion, which he felt was a natural urge and which he defined as a system of morality held in common by a number of people, became purer as it divested itself of theology and approached pure ethics, and as it accommodated itself to the findings of science.

Huxley's outlook in certain respects combined Victorian certainty and respect for traditional morality with a twentieth-century allegiance to science and philosophical skepticism. Huxley, saturated in the scientific spirit, openly questioned the value of any conclusions that did not rest securely upon hard facts obtained through disinterested observation. A doctor by training and a scientist by vocation, he knew firsthand the deadly nature of unsupported generalizations. Yet he often assumes that ethical principles have an objective existence; even that they are self-evident realities.

In many respects Huxley was the most forward-looking of all the great Victorians, but his views in this area are in sharp contrast to those of the twentieth century, which is inclined to consider the subject of ethics and morals as relative and subjective. Words such as "truth," "love," "good," "evil," "right," and "wrong" are sprinkled throughout Huxley's works. In his lecture on Descartes, delivered at the Cambridge YMCA, he de-

clares "that if some great power would agree to make me always
think what is true and do what is right ... I should instantly
close with the offer. The only freedom I care about is the freedom to do right; the freedom to do wrong I am ready to part
with on the cheapest terms to anyone who will take it of me."[7]
Passages such as this continue to be a source of puzzlement to
many critics and commentators.

II *Descartes*

Huxley's high regard for Socrates ("the first agnostic") had its
source in the philosopher's extreme skepticism—but he considered Plato to have been a warper and perverter of his master's
doctrines. The Greeks whom he most admired were the Epi-
cureans and the Stoics. Of the modern thinkers, he most respected Spinoza, who, he thought, reasoned from sound premises
but who frequently became involved in too much unsound
metaphysical speculation. Locke and Hobbes, Huxley felt, were
the first English philosophers to rest their reasoning on a sound
scientific basis. The rational empiricism of Berkeley stands, according to Huxley, between Locke and Hume.

But the two leading figures in Huxley's personal philosophic
pantheon were Hume and Descartes—an unusual combination
since Hume's "mitigated skepticism" was a direct reaction to the
premises of Descartes and his school. Hume indeed is generally
credited with having successfully disposed of the certainties al-
leged by Descartes—matter, soul, existence—and Huxley felt this
criticism of Descartes to have been well taken. But his own
reasons for considering Descartes to be "the father of modern
philosophy" were not the traditional ones. For himself, he saw
Descartes as the first modern philosopher to "consecrate
Doubt." Huxley, nevertheless, maintained important reservations concerning Descartes's *Cogito ergo sum*.

According to Huxley, the statement contains an error in logic;
for the "I am" is already assumed in the "I think"; and the "I
think" presupposes the existence of thought. All Huxley could
say was *Cogito*. Logic aside, this "consecration" of skepticism
was nevertheless a great advance, although still not Descartes's
greatest contribution. Prior to Descartes, philosophers had been
accustomed to approaching their subject matter along the "high

road" of a priori reasoning. And those who attempted to reason inductively—for example, the scholastic philosophers—generally did so from erroneous premises. Huxley felt that abstract speculation must have its roots deep in verified fact; Descartes, Huxley felt, was the first to rest metaphysical principles on the secure basis of scientific observation. It was he—and this contribution, according to Huxley, was his greatest—who postulated the principle that the entire universe, not excepting the actions and thoughts of men, is governed by certain mechanical laws. And upon this principle physical science bases all its assumptions. It was no coincidence, Huxley writes, that the early seventeenth century was the time in which "physical science suddenly strode into the arena of public and familiar thought, and openly challenged not only Philosophy and the Church, but that common ignorance which often passes by the name of Common Sense."[8]

Huxley nevertheless disagrees with certain conclusions reached by the French philosopher. Although certain of his works were placed under the interdiction of Roman authorities, Descartes himself lived and died a Roman Catholic; and Huxley feels that his piety led him to many questionable conclusions. Descartes's distinction between spirit and matter, for example, was without basis. "Matter," according to Descartes, "is substance which has extension but does not think; spirit is substance which thinks, but has no extension." Following Descartes's own premise—that the human body is a machine, the operation of which can be explained entirely by principles of physics—Huxley attempts to demonstrate that no distinction can be made between spirit and matter. Descartes felt that the soul, although it has no extension, can affect the course of action of the animal body. It thereby exerts force; and, since matter in certain forms is itself a series of centers of force, Huxley thinks that Descartes's attempt to distinguish between the two is without foundation.

In his lecture "Animal Automatism" (1874), Huxley expanded and reinforced certain conclusions of Descartes—but chiefly the Cartesian observation that the human body is a machine subject to the same physical laws which govern all other material phenomena. Huxley knew the subject would cause a hostile reaction; and, since the lecture was being given before an avowedly Christian audience, he approached the subject warily—not in the bold fashion he had adopted in "The Physical Basis of Life," when he stood before his audience and dramatically pointed to some vessels in front of him and declared they contained all the ingredients necessary to produce protoplasm and therefore life. Descartes, himself a physiologist, though not on the same level as Harvey, had come to certain conclusions respecting human physiology which were used as the basis for the work of other men for some time thereafter. Huxley evaluates those discoveries of Descartes which helped lay the foundations for the subsequent explanation of the physical processes of life along lines similar to those by which other material phenomena are explained.

One of Descartes's more controversial conclusions had been that brute animals are mere automata devoid of reason and consciousness. Huxley was not inclined to either totally accept or refute this belief, but he did believe that the emotions and ideas of animals could only be explained by molecular changes in the brain which thereby become states of consciousness; and he felt that, by analogy, human states of consciousness similarly are "caused by molecular changes of the brain substance." In this lecture Huxley gives his most illuminating explanation of a time-honored metaphysical dilemma—one which he had approached in the "Physical Basis of Life," as well as in his reply to Mivart and Wallace in "Mr. Darwin's Critics," and which he had touched upon in his YMCA lecture on the French philosopher.

It is easy to see the successive stages of Huxley's thought as it progressed. Darwin had demonstrated the relationship of all species of animal life to one another; Huxley (in *Man's Place in Nature*) had shown man to be kin to apes and by analogy to all animal life. In the "Physical Basis of Life" men were shown to be made of the same substance as inanimate matter and to be subject to the same physical laws; and this principle he had buttressed in the Descartes lecture by defining consciousness as a molecular phenomenon. In "Animal Automatism" he plainly stated the inevitable conclusion: "We are conscious automata, endowed with free will in the only intelligible sense of that

[97]

much abused term—inasmuch as in many respects we are able to do as we like—but none the less parts of the great series of causes and effects which, in unbroken continuity, composes that which is, and has been, and shall be—the sum of existence."[9]

Science had been brought to arbitrate the age-old question over which philosophers and theologians had battled for centuries: whether the actions of men are foreordained or are the result of man's own volition (free will). To Huxley, who thoroughly espoused determinism, man's will and volition were ruled out as a factor in the spinning of the cosmos.[10]

III Hume

The Hume volume, a highly seasoned, readable analysis of Hume's philosophy, is most notable for its lucidity and brevity. The success of the book, Huxley remarked, would depend on what the public would stand of "frank speaking." Huxley did not treat those aspects of Hume's philosophy that he considered to be unimportant or irrelevant. Huxley's approach to philosophy was frankly that of a layman, and the book was directed to a lay audience. Huxley does not hesitate to bring the doctrines of Hume, who died in 1776, into line with the findings of science where necessary; and his corrections are therefore numerous and frequent. Indeed, Huxley's account of the doctrines of Hume illuminates his own philosophy as much as that of his subject; and the book might be described as a kind of collaboration between Hume and Huxley, with frequent nods in the direction of such scientifically minded thinkers as Kant, Descartes, Locke, and Spinoza. Hume's conception of the objectives and limitations of philosophy, Huxley feels, places him between Locke and Kant. But Hume is united with Descartes in his skepticism.[11]

The opening chapters are devoted to a most summary description of Hume's life. "The closest I ever came to writing fiction," Huxley once described this section. Holding his own comments to a minimum, Huxley as a rule allows Hume to speak through his writings. But it is plainly certain eccentric aspects of Hume's character which most fascinate Huxley—for example, his saintliness and his dislike of the English.

In his introduction to the thought of Hume, Huxley argues

[98]

once again the close relationship that must exist between philosophical principles and verified facts. Philosophy, as Huxley conceived it, must rest on a secure foundation of reality. The great hypotheses of philosophy, no less than the great ones of science, must be supported by data acquired through human experience. Philosophy indeed must be considered as a department of science: philosophy deals with what can be known; science, with what is known. Philosophy inquires into the nature of knowledge and into the principles by which scientific method operates. One of Hume's strong points, according to Huxley, was that he recognized the close relationship between philosophy and human nature and that he recognized the ultimate limits of philosophy—that "any hypothesis that pretends to discover the ultimate original qualities of human nature ought at first to be rejected as presumptuous and chimerical." If the great contribution of Descartes was that he inquired into the "nature of certainty," that of Hume was his work toward the establishment of a "science of man."

To the fundamental mental phenomena, termed by Berkeley and Locke "ideas," Hume gave the name "perceptions." Rejecting the traditional notion—considered by Huxley as a legacy of ancient philosophy—that the mind has a separate identity, Hume described it as "a heap or collection of different perceptions." To the irresolvable states of consciousness Hume gave the name "impressions," under which he included the five senses, as well as pain and pleasure. Hume used the word "idea" to describe any memory or expectation of an "impression." An idea, according to Hume, is of necessity a copy of an impression; and man's conceptions have their origin in the world outside the mind. Man receives his conception of a straight line, for example, from nature, which provides us with the initial raw material for the "idea" of a straight line. Somewhat amending Hume's hypothesis, Huxley describes the perceptions—including the recognition of relationships between them—as the basic raw materials of knowledge.

On the origins of the impressions, as well as on the question of innate ideas, Huxley suggests that Hume offered no improvement on the thought of Descartes. Because Hume's acquaintance with the science of physiology was slight, his lack of knowledge led him into a number of contradictions. What Hume called the operations of the mind ("perceptions") are brought about, Huxley argues, by antecedent changes in the matter of the brain; and matter and motion are, in the last analysis, responsible for sensations, ideas, and emotions. Hume, according to Huxley, leaned in this respect in the direction of Descartes; but his terminology, when dealing with the question is, by Huxley's estimate, vague and unsatisfactory. And the same is true of Hume's writing on innate ideas. The potentialities for the contents of the mind, Huxley declares, are within it, and experience merely calls these potentialities into existence. An experience sets into operation a mechanism of the mind which generates a certain class of thoughts. Huxley believes that a particular experience or, as is frequently the case, one thought calls another thought into existence through the process of association. Hume's failure to advance a comprehensive theory in this respect can be attributed, Huxley felt, largely to his failure to recognize the significance of the physiological experiments of Descartes.

These operations of the mind are not dependent on language. Children before they can speak are able to frame mental propositions and to act upon them. The child's experience of tasting a sugar plum, for example, sets the mechanism of the mind into operation: "The child ... cannot say sugar plum was sweet; yet the psychical operation of which that proposition is merely the verbal expression is perfectly effected." The child's mind has come to possess the idea; the child has only to learn to use language to be able to put it into words. The possession of the idea is what is known as "memory," and it occasions the belief that another sugar plum will be sweet. This belief is what is known as an "expectation." Expectations, therefore, may be defined as inverted memories.

As might be anticipated, the scientifically minded Huxley is often critical of the vagueness of Hume's terminology. In discussing Hume's work in comparative psychology—the philosopher was not in accord with Descartes in attributing thought and reason to animals—Huxley, while generally in agreement, nevertheless is critical of Hume's use of such words as "instinct." The processes by which mental phenomena of animals are realized, Huxley says, are analogous to those of human beings. But the potentialities of, say, a child and a dog are what differentiate them—the potential of the human mind, of course, being much greater.

Huxley was far from being an uncritical follower of Hume, but about the subject of religion they were in closest agreement. Huxley shared Hume's dislike for theology (and theologians), but the former felt that Hume failed to differentiate sufficiently between theology and religion. Not surprisingly, Huxley shows himself to be most acute in his discussions of Hume's views on miracles.

Hume's famous attack rested simply on the premise that beliefs and expectations are derived from generations of uniform experience. Any event antagonistic to this uniform experience required full proof of its having occurred to be accepted. According to Hume, no event deserving of the appellation "miraculous" could produce such verification. In other words, Hume's argument—which Huxley does not hesitate to label as "absurd" —can be stated as that which has never been known by men to have occurred never can occur.

Hume defined a miracle as a "violation of the laws of nature," and Huxley argues that doing so was his basic error. The definition is an example of the misuse of language, "for 'nature' means neither more nor less than that which is: the sum of phenomena presented to our experience; the totality of events past, present, and to come." No law is violated by an experience which is contrary to expectation and to the uniform record of human experience. The occurrence of such an unanticipated event merely results in the enlargement of human experience and in a modification of what can be expected to take place in the future. It was only when Hume directed his argument against belief in a particular miracle that it had any value. In order to believe in an occurrence which conflicts with experience, one does indeed require sounder testimony and in a ratio within the degree of improbability of the occurrence. Hume's conclusion that there are no miracles on record which are substantiated by satisfactory evidence is affirmed by Huxley.

It was probably in the area of theism that Hume had his greatest effect on Huxley. Hume's views on the subject of a "creator" are those of a good agnostic and, Huxley declares, "included as little as possible of affirmation, respecting a problem which he felt to be hopelessly insoluble." For reasons similar to those responsible for Hume's reluctance to speculate on the nature of a "first cause," he expressed doubt as to the existence of a soul. In such matters, logic and reason are powerless and should remain silent.

Hume and Huxley are also united in their determinism: "The more one knows of the real conditions which determine men's acts, the less one finds in them to praise or blame." Certainly man—a finite being—can be capable of no deed that merits either infinite suffering or infinite happiness. And, concerning the ancient philosophical dilemma of free will and necessity, Hume's philosophy reduces it to mere wordplay. The conflict between them arises from hazy terminology. Man quite plainly has freedom—within limits. But, to disprove the necessitarian argument, an individual would have to associate "any emotion whatever with any idea whatever; to like pain as much as pleasure; vice as much as virtue; in short, to prove that, whatever may be the fixity of the order of the universe of things, that of thought is given over to chance."[12]

Huxley had intended to expand his two articles on Berkeley— "Bishop Berkeley on the Metaphysics of Sensation" and "Sensation and the Unity of Structures of Sensiferous Organs"[13]— into a companion volume to his Hume book; but other work prevented his fulfilling the project. However, in his *Collected Essays* he appended the essays to his Hume volume; and they contain ample evidence to show why Huxley—who was no less enthusiastic in his admiration for Berkeley than in his admiration for Hume—held the clergyman in such high regard. With Hume and Hobbes, Huxley considered Berkeley to be among the three greatest English thinkers; and, coming from the generally curmudgeonly Huxley, such words are high praise. Like Descartes, Berkeley recognized that the roots of philosophy lie among the facts of physiology—and, specifically, within that branch of physiology which deals with the organs of sensation.

In his preface to the Hume volume Huxley described Berkeley as having "carried out to its logical result the Cartesian principle, that absolute certainty attaches only to the knowledge of facts of consciousness." Berkeley's criticism of philosophical materialism was, according to Huxley, irrefutable. What one knows of matter and motion is known only through sensations and reflections—in other words, only as "forms of consciousness." One's faculties impose absolute limitations on one's knowledge of phenomena.

CHAPTER 6

An Eminent Controversialist

BEGINNING in 1880 the pressure of official business upon Huxley grew steadily greater, reaching its height in 1883. The necessity to devote more and more time to administrative work coincided with a decline in vigor; and his original work—especially scientific—was the chief sufferer. In 1883 he was able to produce only one scientific paper. His official obligations for the day discharged, Huxley would take a taxi to his laboratory to work for a half hour over his dissections. But more and more projects remained unfinished, and laboratory work often was left untouched for months at a time.

In April he fell ill but recovered quickly. Then in July he contracted an additional responsibility: he allowed himself to be named President of the Royal Society, an honor which he was unable to refuse but a post for which he could hardly spare energy or time—and Mrs. Huxley was strongly opposed to her husband's taking the position. Huxley's reasons for accepting the post are contained in a letter to a fellow scientist: "I will not if I can help it, allow the chair of the Royal Society to become the apenage [*sic*] of rich men, or have the noble old Society exploited by enterprising commercial gents who make their profit out of the application of science."[1] But these words only tell half the story, since the presidency represented the very pinnacle of honors for a scientific man, and Huxley doubtless derived more satisfaction from the honor than he ever dared to admit.

Huxley's illness in April, while not serious, was a harbinger of the fact that the dyspepsia which had haunted him during the 1870's was once more to afflict him. In 1884 his condition took a serious turn; scientific work was abandoned altogether since even the physical exertion involved in peering into a microscope now caused him serious discomfort, and some four years were to elapse before he would publish another scientific paper. He also curtailed his official duties by resigning from a number of minor posts. Among the offices dropped was that of the presidency of the National Association of Science Teachers, a position whose duties wanted "sharp looking after." For perhaps the first time in his life he was removing more irons from the fire than he was putting in.

Between April and July Huxley's post as Inspector of Fisheries required him to do a good deal of traveling. In August he withdrew to Surrey, where he occupied himself principally with the preparation of a new edition of *Lessons in Elementary Physiology*. Indeed, his work at this time was his chief consolation. "So long as I sit still," he wrote to Michael Foster,[2] "and write or read I am all right, otherwise not good for much, which is odd, considering that I eat, drink, and sleep like a top."[3]

I   *Retirement*

Huxley made a game effort to hold his post at the School of Mines in the fall of 1884. It had been his intention to wind up his teaching career at the conclusion of the academic year the following spring, at which time he would have been one month past sixty and would have completed thirty-one years with the school. But the physical strain involved in giving two weeks of lectures brought him to the point of total collapse. He was ordered by his doctor to relinquish all his duties and to proceed immediately to the Continent to recuperate. Most of the following seven months were spent shuttling from town to town in Italy, dodging a plague of cholera which had descended upon the Italian peninsula. Besides the cholera epidemic, the trip was complicated by the Italian winter, which was exceptionally cold, and he spent much of his time shivering in poorly heated hotel rooms.

Huxley's letters are full of melancholy comments which reflect the sorry state of his mind and body. Venice he rather enjoyed, and Rome, after he had gotten over his initial disenchantment, he found "wonderfully interesting." But he reacted to the endless number of churches and art galleries with little enthusiasm. In fact, his saturation was such that in a letter to his daughter he described himself as beginning to feel a "dislike for the Fine Arts generally. Perhaps after a week or two I shall take to science out of sheer weariness."[4] All in all, he was quite relieved to return to England the following April. The fact that the winter had not been pleasant is borne out by the moral he drew from his "vacation": "If you are perfectly well and strong, brave Italy— but in search of health stay home."[5]

If the stay on the Continent achieved nothing else, it had persuaded Huxley of the necessity of immediate retirement. On May 11, 1885, he gave official notice to the School of Mines. The retirement of the institution's most illustrious faculty member was an occasion of great sadness at South Kensington, but the officials responded nobly to the occasion. They showed their appreciation for Huxley's three decades of extraordinary service by adroitly pulling a number of strategic wires and by arranging to have him retired on a number of pensions which would provide him with an income equivalent to his former salary.

Moreover, his connection with the school was not entirely severed. He was granted the title Honorary Dean and retained his old title, Professor of Biology. The following November at the anniversary meeting of the Royal Society he asked in his last presidential address "to be permitted to vacate the chair of the Society as soon as the business of this meeting is at an end." The professional career that had begun with his entrance into the navy in April, 1846, was officially ended after four decades. One of the privileges that came with retirement was the right to speak freely and openly for unpopular causes without being regarded as the spokesman for a particular association or institution. Having divested himself of his Royal Society and School of Mines connections, Huxley was freer in this respect after 1885 than he had ever been before. Not that he had ever permitted such considerations to keep him out of the controversial arena or to deter him from defending unpopular ideas, but his controversial activities were never greater than in the last decade of his life. Indeed, except for his militant championing of Darwin, Huxley is best remembered today for his hectic theological controversies with William Gladstone and other defenders of religious orthodoxy. Huxley's work as a scientist was much more significant and far-reaching than his polemics, but the unalloyed brilliance he exhibited—the variety and depth of his learning, his gift for manufacturing apt and cutting phrases—in these battles has been remembered where his more workman-like contributions to the store of human knowledge have been forgotten.

II *Early Controversies*

The first contemporary to feel the impact of Huxley's rhetoric had been the inoffensive Robert Chambers when Huxley had reviewed *The Vestiges* in 1854. Next was Richard Owen, upon whom Huxley had descended in the Royal Society's Croomian Lecture four years later, and with whom he had engaged in a ludicrous debate concerning the resemblances between anthropoid and pithecoid craniums for nearly five years. Huxley's most famous public debate, of course, had been conducted at Oxford in 1860, when he had made his deft retort to Bishop Wilberforce. Subsequently, he had engaged St. George Mivart in the pages of *The Contemporary Review*, and from time to time he had found it necessary to comment on assertions which ran counter to his own views. Sometimes, in fact, his statements were quite sharp; in 1870, for example, *The Spectator* reprimanded Huxley for the tone he used to answer a correspondent to the *Pall Mall Gazette*.

A gentleman signing himself "Devonshire Man" had written a letter to the periodical registering his disagreement with a statement Huxley had made in a public lecture, "Forefathers and Forerunners of the English People." Huxley had stated that "Devonshire men are as little Anglo-Saxons as Northumbrians are Welsh," and the correspondent in his reply had not limited himself strictly to matters of science. This tactical mistake was to prove fatal; for Huxley, in replying, also felt free to adopt a personal tone. "A Devonshire Man," he wrote in reply, "is good enough to say of me that 'cutting up monkeys is his forte, and cutting up men is his foible.' With your permission, I propose to cut up a Devonshire Man; but I leave to the public to judge whether, when so employed, my occupation is to be referred to the former or latter category."[6]

Most of these early controversies—with Owen, Wallace, and St. George Mivart—were outgrowths of his campaign of propaganda on behalf of Darwin. In 1868, however, as a result of some remarks made in "The Physical Basis of Life," he was drawn into a mild skirmish with a small but articulate group of English admirers of Auguste Comte. Comte's writings at the time were the subject of extravagant praise (G. H. Lewes, for example, saluted an English translation of his work as marking the dawn of "a new era"); and among his followers could be counted such influential men as John Morley and Frederic Harrison. The extent of Morley's interest in Comtean Positivism is reflected by the fact that the *Fortnightly,* the magazine of which he was editor, was during 1869 and 1870 a veritable battlefield of Positivist and anti-Positivist controversy. In his lecture, Huxley had directed some sharp criticism at Comte, saying he found in his philosophy "little or nothing of any scientific value, and a great deal which is as thoroughly antagonistic to the very essence of science as anything in ultramontane Catholicism. In fact, M. Comte's philosophy, in practice, might be compendiously described as Catholicism *minus* Christianity."[7]

Comte aimed at a system based not on theology but on science; but, as Huxley was quick to recognize, the Frenchman's acquaintance with the physical sciences was limited to what he had acquired through reading. Huxley's irreverent critique drew a rejoinder from Richard Congreve, the Oxford historian and translator of Comte, who in a ponderous "Mr. Huxley on M. Comte," in the *Fortnightly Review* for April, 1869, declared that Huxley's lack of respect for Comte was due to his not having read him.[8] Congreve accused Huxley of taking a narrow view of the term "science," and he suggested that he repent his hastily formulated opinions. Congreve's inability to associate disapproval of his master with anything but ignorance proved fatal, for Huxley immediately extended his criticism of Comte to include Congreve.

Replying at length in "The Scientific Aspects of Positivism" (*Fortnightly,* February, 1869), Huxley declared that he had been acquainted with the works of Comte for "some sixteen or seventeen years"; and he then developed his original hypothesis —Comte's "bulky volumes" contained "little or nothing of any scientific value." Huxley was willing to grant that, from the standpoint of sociology, Comte's work was not without value; but his knowledge of science was superficial and secondhand;

"What struck me was his want of apprehension of the great features of science; his strange mistakes as to the merits of his scientific contemporaries; and his ludicrously erroneous notions about the part which some of the scientific doctrines current in his time were destined to play in the future."[9]

Huxley, moreover, saw no reason to retract his epigrammatic evaluation of the Positivistic philosophy. "Comte's ideal," according to Huxley, "is Catholic organization without Catholic doctrine, or, in other words, Catholicism *minus* Christianity. Surely it is utterly unjustifiable to ascribe to one base motives for stating a man's doctrines . . . in his own words." Huxley's clever evaluation of Comteism, which received a certain amount of currency in the years following, is credited with having a damaging effect on the Comtean cause in England.[10]

III *Interpreters of Genesis*

The summer of 1884 was not a happy one for Huxley since he continued to be plagued by ill health and since his disinclination to pursue science left him with too much leisure. With the intention of usefully occupying this time, he developed a new interest—or he renewed an old interest. "I am principally occupied in studying the gospels," he wrote to Foster from Surrey in August; and this renewel interest in theology involved him in a now almost legendary controversy—the exchange with William Gladstone in the *Nineteenth Century* which began during the fall of 1885.

The summer of 1885 was enlivened by the appearance of the English translation of the *Prolegomena to the History of Religion* by the French critic Albert Réville. To give offense to the Victorians, a book, it often seemed, needed only to be scientific. Among the works which over the course of the century had an unsettling effect were Lyell's *The Principles of Geology*, Chambers' *Vestiges*, Darwin's *Origin*, and Huxley's *Man's Place in Nature*. Réville's book caused a stir not because it said anything new but because of the matter-of-fact tone of the author and his disconcerting habit of supporting his godless theories with evidence. The principal argument of the work was that the account of creation contained in Genesis enjoyed the status of a myth but could in no way be regarded as an authentic description of the origin of life.

Among those who felt that Réville's eminently scientific tone was not justified by the findings of science was Prime Minister of England William Gladstone; and in "The Dawn of Creation and of Worship," in the *Nineteenth Century* for November, 1885, he said so. According to Gladstone, there was nothing in Dr. Réville's criticism "but what tends to confirm .... the old-fashioned belief that there is a revelation in the Book of Genesis." The order of creation—described in Genesis as taking place on the fifth and sixth day—Gladstone asserted to be in harmony with the findings of science. The water population, created first, was followed by the air and land population and, finally, by man; and such was his assurance that he felt the burden of proof lay with the skeptic. He concluded his article with a sneer at Darwin: evolution was not a new doctrine but could be found in the writings of St. Paul and St. Augustine. "It may be true, may be delightful and wonderful in its right place," but for Gladstone it had the unhappy effect of dethroning mind and spirit from their old supremacy.

Gladstone, of course, was a unique combination of naïveté and ultrasophistication. His almost childish devotion to the Scriptures, which was legendary, was just one of the many extraordinary facets of his remarkable character. He was one who, to quote his own words, "tread the floor of the earth with an upward and not a downward eye." Such unremitting orthodoxy plainly was not calculated to endear him to Huxley; however, Huxley's feelings toward England's "Grand Old Man" were ambivalent and seemed to parallel earlier feelings toward Sir Richard Owen. Huxley had thought highly of Owen's ability as a scientist but had had serious reservations toward his character.[11] As for Gladstone, Huxley thought he was possessed of a pronounced streak of demagoguery; but he could not help admiring his ability as a politician. "I should like to know," Huxley said once in a burst of spontaneous admiration, "what would keep such a man as that back; why put him in the middle of a moor, with nothing in the world but his shirt, and you could not prevent him from being anything he liked."[12]

The two men had become personally acquainted some fifteen

years before at the meetings of the Metaphysical Society—at which time Huxley had wryly questioned Gladstone's credentials for membership. Queried on Gladstone's knowledge of metaphysics, Huxley is reported to have declared: "Metaphysics? He does not know the meaning of the term."[13] And Huxley on more than one occasion was heavily critical of Gladstone's conduct as a public man, particularly of his eagerness to ingratiate himself with the masses. Gladstone practiced what Huxley described as the "watch dog theory of premiership ... The theory, I mean, that the whole duty of a political chief is to look sharp for the way the social coach is driving, and then run in front and bark loud."[14]

Huxley replied to Gladstone's apologetics in the *Nineteenth Century* of the following month. His article "The Interpreters of Genesis and the Interpreters of Nature" contains nothing new—a failing, perhaps, that was not to be avoided. In 1871 in "Mr. Darwin's Critics" Huxley had delivered his opinion on the conflict between scientific and biblical cosmogonies; and in "Lectures on Evolution," five years later, he had advanced a great deal of paleontological evidence to demonstrate that the Mosaic writer's account of creation was not a literal one. In a letter to a friend, Huxley described his motives for replying to Gladstone; from the point of view of science, Gladstone's article was a negligible effort, "not worth powder and shot." But the prestige of the Grand Old Man was enormous, and his words carried tremendous influence. "The ignorance of the so-called educated classes in this country is stupendous," Huxley wrote in explanation; "and in the hands of people like Gladstone it is a political force."[15]

Gladstone's thesis was contradicted at many points by the very authorities he cited in his support, but his persuasive rhetoric could not be so easily dismissed. Huxley felt that the liberties Gladstone had taken with scientific data could have a distinctly mischievous effect on the current of English thought. As a result, Huxley, in "The Interpreters of Genesis and the Interpreters of Nature,"[16] attempts to refute the order of creation advanced by Gladstone by an appeal to the fossil evidence.

Huxley concludes his argument with an evaluation of the antagonism between science and religion—an antagonism which he feels is fabricated and not inevitable: "fabricated, on the one hand, by short-sighted religious people who confound a certain branch of science, theology, with religion; and, on the other, by equally short-sighted scientific people who forget that science takes for its province only that which is susceptible of clear intellectual comprehension; and that, outside the boundaries of that province, they must be content with imagination, with hope, and with ignorance."[17] Despite the inferior quality of his essay, Huxley was quite pleased with it. "Do read my polishing off of the G. O. M.," he adjured Spencer. "I am proud of it as a work and as evidence that the volcano is not yet exhausted."[18]

Gladstone replied in the *Nineteenth Century* for January in "Prome to Genesis."[19] Gladstone thanked Huxley for the clarifying scientific data contained in his article, apologized for the lack of scientific terminology in his own writing, and then went on to reassert his original proposition. His second contribution was a bit more subdued in tone (a reflection of surprise, perhaps, that Huxley had decided to enter the argument), and it did not contain the sharp criticisms of Darwinian theory contained in "The Dawn of Creation and Worship."

The manuscript of Huxley's second reply to Gladstone, "Mr. Gladstone and Genesis," contained so many jibes at the Prime Minister that the article caused some alarm in the editorial offices of the *Nineteenth Century*. Knowles returned it to Huxley, who revised it to make it more acceptable in content. Nevertheless, the general tone of his rejoinder is one of irreverence; and the following hilarious passage is typical of his satirical manner:

Socrates is reported to have said of the works of Heraclitus that ... what he could understand was so good that he was disposed to believe in the excellence of that which he found unintelligible. In endeavouring to make myself master of Mr. Gladstone's meaning on these pages, I have often been overcome by a feeling analogous to that of Socrates, but not quite the same. That which I do understand has appeared to me so very much the reverse of good, that I have sometimes permitted myself to doubt the value of that which I do not understand.[20]

But this article suffers from the same failings as "The Interpreters of Genesis and the Interpreters of Nature"—too much elementary exposition. Indeed, it was by now apparent that little was to be gained by continuing the controversy. Gladstone did not reply, and Huxley's next article was "The Evolution of Theology" (*Nineteenth Century,* March and April, 1886). However, his dislike for Gladstone had been seriously aggravated by the exchange; and, when Gladstone's Home Rule Bill was voted down in Parliament the following July, Huxley exulted over his defeat. "The smashing of the G. O. M." he told Michael Foster, "appears to be pretty complete, though he has unfortunately enough left to give him the means of playing an ugly game of obstruction in the next Parliament."[21]

IV *Science and Morals*

After "polishing off" Gladstone, Huxley found it necessary to retire to Bournemouth. The "English Naples" did not offer a climate much more congenial than that of London, but his health improved sufficiently for him to return to the city early in April. After only a few weeks, however, he was once more in flight before his "blue devils." He now sought health in the bracing winds of the moors at Ilkey in Yorkshire, which years earlier had also been a favorite retreat of Darwin's. Huxley found the moors delightful, and he began spending more and more time outdoors. "I took a three hours' walk this morning," he wrote to his wife on April 27, "with nothing but grouse and peeweets for company, and it was perfectly delicious. I am beginning to forget that I have a liver."[22] Huxley remained, with the exception of a few weeks, in Yorkshire for the next three months.

The latter part of the summer was spent in Switzerland, where he developed an interest in gentians, a pursuit that resulted in "The Gentians: Notes and Queries." When the article was published in 1887, it was the first scientific work he had produced in four years. But he had more than enough obligations to keep him busy. During the fall of 1886 he was occupied with "The Reception of the Origin of Species" for the Darwin biography, with a chapter on "The Progress of Science" for *The Reign of Victoria,* and with "Science and Morals" for the *Fortnightly.*

The last article was a reply to "Materialism and Morality" by W. S. Lilly, which had appeared in the *Fortnightly.* Dr. Lilly had referred to Huxley, Spencer, and W. K. Clifford as spokesmen for a materialistic view of phenomena which, were it to continue unchecked, would lead to the downfall of civilization. "Morality in Professor Huxley, I can well believe, is strong enough to hold its own," Dr. Lilly had written. "But will it be strong enough in Professor Huxley's grandchildren?" Lilly charged Huxley, Spencer, and Clifford with holding as unverifiable everything which was beyond the bounds of physical science and which could not be verified by the senses. Lilly held the precepts of morality to be absolute and to require supernatural sanction if they were to carry any authority.

Lilly's representation of Huxley's views was not unfair, and his own concern for the future of morality was shared by many eminent contemporaries. What most bothered Huxley, however, was the attribution to him of a "materialistic" philosophy: "My creed [he wrote in reply] may be an ill-favoured thing, but it is mine own, as Touchstone says of his ladylove; and I have so high an opinion of the solid virtues of the object of my affections that I cannot calmly see her personated by a wench who is much uglier and has no virtue worth speaking of."[23]

Huxley concedes that there are many areas of phenomena—for example, that of consciousness and "the strange rapture of beauty" offered by nature and art—which physical science will forever be at a loss to explain. He concludes by equating physical science with Cinderella: "She lights the fire, sweeps the house, and provides the dinner; and is rewarded by being told she is a base creature, devoted to low and material interests." The two ugly sisters—the villains of the parable—are theology and philosophy.

Many years earlier Huxley had described himself as "abominating" the word "law." It was, in fact, not so much the word he disliked as its misuse in philosophic and scientific contexts. Abuse of the word was a mark of what he liked to call "pseudo-science"—to be found in "the writings of those who have appropriated the forms of science without knowing anything of its substance." People regarded "laws" of nature as agents and causes rather than as generalized records of experience and probability. This misuse of terminology had been responsible for much confused thinking among philosophers, theologians, and even scientists. Geologists, for example, late in the nineteenth century had been in the habit of falling back on the word "catastrophe" to account for conditions which they were at a loss to explain and of employing the word as a catch-all to describe occurrences which were outside the normal course of events.

In the fall of 1886 Canon Liddon, a prominent Anglican clergyman, in a sermon at St. Paul's attempted to justify the possibility of divinely ordained catastrophes by offering as an explanation the suspension of certain physical laws by the intervention of other, higher laws. In "Pseudo-Scientific Realism" Huxley—without mentioning the preacher's name—pointed to the fallacy in his argument: a natural event cannot be conceived of as being a contravention of a natural law. As a particular illustration he took Newton's widely known theories of gravitation. Bodies, Huxley asserted, do not fall to the ground because of the law of gravity: "The law is simply a record of the fact ... they have so fallen ... and a reasonable expectation that they will so fall."[24] Abuse of the term Huxley described as a by-product of scholastic realism; while science regards all phenomena as intimately and logically connected, the schoolmen perceived a duality in the universe—a sensible world and a supersensible world—and the former, they felt, was inferior and subject to the latter.

The following month the *Fortnightly* contained a wordy article entitled "Professor Huxley on Canon Liddon." Huxley's remarks on the misuse of scientific terminology had, it seemed, given offense to the Duke of Argyll, the author of a widely read book, *Reign of Law,* who apparently recognized himself as guilty of many of the errors cited by Huxley. And Argyll, who had been elected to the Royal Society at the age of twenty-eight, exhibits on this occasion many unscientific habits of mind. "Professor Huxley on Canon Liddon" is long on eloquence but short on sound reasoning. According to Huxley, who replied in "Science and Pseudo-Science," the Duke entertained many serious misconceptions regarding the fundamentals of science. Among them was a failure to comprehend the meaning of geological uniformitarianism, Newton's theories of gravitation, and certain theories of Kepler.

And then there was the Duke's own book, *Reign of Law.* Huxley ventures the opinion that the Duke had entered the debate chiefly because Huxley's original criticisms had found their mark in the doctrines of the Duke himself. One of the sillier points raised by the Duke was the prophecy of a forthcoming revolt in the world of science against a "reign of terror" inspired by the authority of Darwin. When His Grace even predicted that Huxley would soon join the revolt openly, Huxley almost had no choice but to conclude his rejoinder on a facetious note: "I am sure the Duke of Argyll will be glad to hear that the anxiety he created was of extremely short duration. It is my privilege to have access to the best sources of information, and nobody in the scientific world can tell me anything about either the 'Reign of Terror' or 'The Revolt.' In fact, the scientific world laughs most undecorously at the notion of the existence of either...."[25]

With the arrival of summer Huxley again departed for the Continent where, in Switzerland, he renewed his study of gentians. But, if he thought his reply had permanently silenced the Duke, he had clearly underestimated the persistence of the nobleman. He returned to England to find "A Great Lesson" in the *Fortnightly* for September; and this article was, if anything, even more perfervid and eloquent than "Professor Huxley on Canon Liddon." Principally an attempt to denigrate Darwin's reputation as a scientist, the new article contained a groundless criticism of Darwin's theory on the formation of coral reefs. In truth, the Duke knew just enough about science to make a fool of himself when he ventured to write about it.

Huxley was not inclined to continue the debate with the Duke, but he appended a rebuttal at the conclusion of "An Episcopal Trilogy" (*Fortnightly*, November, 1887). The Duke contended that Darwin's theory of coral reefs had been disproved by John Murray. Some years had, in fact, elapsed since Huxley had last been an advocate of Darwin, but he now demonstrated well enough that he was not without the old fire. James Dwight Dana, the American oceanographer, had in fact weighed the theories of Darwin against those of Murray and had favored the former. Huxley indicates that Argyll's criticism of Darwin, since he was unaware of Dana's work, was unforgivable ignorance.[26]

At the meeting of the British Association for the Advancement of Science in Manchester in 1887, three bishops delivered sermons on the relationship between science and religion. Huxley's "An Episcopal Trilogy," chiefly an evaluation of the sentiments of the bishops, indicates he was quite pleased by the hospitality to science and scientists that he detected in the sermons of the churchmen. Indeed, he was so anxious to show himself in accord with the clergymen he went so far as to deny any "inconsistency between the acceptance of the constancy of natural order and a belief in the efficacy of prayer." For himself, he did not think it probable that there was a "a finite being who plays with the solar systems as a child plays with a toy."[27] But he felt that strongly held convictions—regardless of their intrinsic worth —have a favorable effect on "the direction and intensity of our intellectual and moral convictions."

This article appeared in the November *Nineteenth Century*. On November 29 he was scheduled to deliver an address on technical education at Manchester. Ten days before, however, he was notified of the death of his daughter, Marian, of pneumonia. Although she had been in ill health for a number of years, the shock to Huxley was still a grave one. For a time he considered postponing the speaking engagement—which involved a four-hundred-mile trip—but at last he decided to fulfill the obligation, although it meant leaving his wife. He had been looking forward to the anniversary meeting of the Royal Society—where Sir Joseph Hooker was to receive the Copley Medal—to be held the following day, but it was necessary to return to Mrs. Huxley, so that he was forced to forgo the occasion. Nevertheless, he was glad he had made the trip. "I have the satisfaction of having got through a hard bit of work," he writes to Foster on his return, "and am none the worse physically—rather the better for having to pull myself together."[28]

V *Agnostic Essays*

The man who coins a word that finds a permanent place in the language is assured of a kind of immortality; for, as long as the word remains in the lexicon, the chances are that the memory of the man responsible for originating it will remain alive. Not that Huxley needed this kind of immortality, but the manner in which he came to coin that very useful term "agnostic" (useful especially for the twentieth century) is too good to pass by.

The necessity, as he told the story in his essay "Agnosticism,"[29] arose during his term of membership in the Metaphysical Society. The society's various members represented just about every faction of philosophical, theological, and political thought. This situation made Huxley acutely aware that he, almost alone, was not a spokesman for any particular "ism"; and for this reason he sought a suitably descriptive word to describe his own intellectual position. The word "agnostic" suggested itself, he said in the essay, because it was "antithetic to the 'gnostic' of Church history, who professed to know so much about the very things of which I was ignorant; and I took the earliest opportunity of parading it at our Society, to show that I, too, had a tail, like the other foxes."

Whether or not the Church Congress had convened in the fall of 1888, it is likely that Huxley sooner or later would have produced an article along the lines of "Agnosticism." The essay contains much material that he was apparently quite anxious to express, and he responded with alacrity when one of the clergymen provided him with an opportunity to do so. The publication in 1888 of *Robert Elsmere* by Mrs. Humphrey Ward, a book that had been nearly as great a shock to orthodox Victorians as the *Origin,* had given new impetus to godless speculation in England.

Mrs. Ward's novel recounted the story of an idealistic young clergyman who finds his faith is not strong enough to withstand the many rationalist and skeptical arguments which were permeating the air of nineteenth-century England. Disenchanted and confused, he gives up his living, founds a new religion based on charity and humanism, and dedicates his life to helping the poor in the London slums. There was no question that, despite its melodramatic overtones, the book had accurately reflected the spiritual confusion and agony of many Englishmen.

For this reason the delegates to the Church Congress devoted one of their sessions to special consideration of atheism, agnosticism, and pessimism. Verbatim reports of the proceedings were contained in the Official Report of the Church Congress, and the divines seem to have succumbed to the heady atmosphere that often seems at convention time to grip political delegates and businessmen. In the course of the afternoon's business, W. C.

Magee, Bishop of Peterborough, delivered a talk in which, to the enthusiastic applause of the clerics, he denounced agnosticism as "cowardly" and coined therewith a phrase that was to enjoy a good deal of currency. But, by all reports, Henry Wace, D.D., Principal of Kings College, London, stole the spotlight. In a talk, "On Agnosticism," he traced the history of the word (not omitting to mention the name of the man who had coined it), and then analyzed the character and motives of those who so describe themselves. "He may prefer to call himself an agnostic," Dr. Wace said dramatically, "but his real name is an older one—he is an infidel."

When Huxley read the Church Congress report, the remarks of the divines were all that were required to free him from the cocoon of melancholy which had enveloped him during the winter. He responded with "Agnosticism," which was printed in the *Nineteenth Century* for February, 1889. He based the agnostic argument chiefly on the question of testimony. The divinity of Christ does not rest on His authority but on that of those who have related the story of His life—the compilers of the Gospels. Huxley makes particular reference to the story of the Gadarene swine. Common sense inclines all honest men to be skeptical of the literal truth of a tale which holds that demons were caused to be removed from a man and to enter into a herd of swine, belief in demons being "pretty much in the inverse ratio of the general instruction, intelligence and sound judgment of the population among whom it prevails." The second Gospel reports Christ to have said: "Come forth, thou unclean spirit, out of the man."

If the report is accurate, Jesus is unhappily convicted of a belief in demons; if not, Huxley concludes, the truth of the story itself falls into question and, along with it, that of the balance of the New Testament. Huxley describes himself as being unable to find any "escape from this dilemma: either Jesus said what he is reported to have said, or he did not. In the former case, it is inevitable that his authority on matters connected with the unseen world should be roughly shaken; in the latter, the blow falls upon the authority of the synoptic Gospels."

This essay also contains Huxley's definition of agnosticism. Huxley denies that it is a creed; instead, he says, it is a way of

thinking and is as old as Socrates. "It is," he writes, "the foundation of the Reformation, which simply illustrated the axiom
that every man should be able to give a reason for the faith that
is within him; it is the great principle of Descartes; it is the fundamental axiom of modern science." Agnosticism, as Huxley
had originally employed the term, signified simply a reservation
of judgment in matters not subject to verification. Here, however, he equates the word with the principle of the Reformation
—"every man should be able to give a reason for the faith that is
within him"—and is guilty of distortion of the original meaning. The word is plainly being used too generally when it can
be applied to Luther, Descartes, Socrates, and as the fundamental
hypothesis of modern science.

The first person to quarrel with Huxley about his use of the
word was W. H. Mallock who, in an ironically titled article in
the April *Fortnightly,* "Cowardly Agnosticism," declared the
word meant "precisely what Professor Huxley says it does not
mean. It means a creed, it means a faith, it means a religious or
irreligious philosophy. And this is the meaning attributed to it
by the world at large, but in reality by Professor Huxley also
quite as much as anybody." For a while, it seemed that no two
people could agree on exactly what an agnostic was.

Such was the interest in the question, however, that the periodicals of England were filled with commentaries on the controversy. Frederic Harrison wrote an article for the January *Fortnightly* on "The Future of Agnosticism," and Gladstone had
contributed a criticism of Mrs. Ward's novel, "Robert Elsmere
and the Battle of Belief," to the *Nineteenth Century* shortly after
the book's publication. Indeed, Knowles's periodical for a time
was dedicated as exclusively to airing the controversy as the *Fortnightly* under Morley had been to printing articles about Positivism. All told, no less than nine articles on some aspect of the
question found their way into the periodical's pages between
February and June.

Huxley doubtless chose the story of the Gadarene pigs because he felt it to be somewhat ludicrous (he once referred to
it as "preposterous and immoral") and, therefore, easily controverted. This miracle, however, far from being a cornerstone
of Christian teaching, is not an essential article of the Christian

faith. Principal Wace raised this point in his reply, "Agnosti-cism, a Reply to Professor Huxley."[30] Huxley, he alleges, only used the question of the veracity of the account as an evasion tactic. Central to Christianity was belief in the Lord's Prayer, the Sermon on the Mount, and the Passion of Christ. In the bargain, the clergyman showed himself to be familiar with the works of quite a few Continental biblical critics, as well as the possessor of a forceful personality and a vigorous writing style.

Huxley responded with "Agnosticism: A Rejoinder,"[31] a long, poorly organized article in which he once again tries to reduce the case against belief in the Gospels to a question of testimony. In truth, there is little in it that he had not said better on some other occasion. He restates his old arguments to discredit the Sermon on the Mount and the Lord's Prayer; and, after an un-flattering analysis of the character of Paul, Huxley concludes that he must be discounted as a reliable witness to the events surrounding the death of Christ. Huxley describes the obstacles to believing these stories as "insuperable" and declares himself unable to comprehend how men of good will and good sense can give them credence. The latter portion of the essay is de-voted to a discursive attempt to show how the original teachings of Jesus have been warped by generations of theologians. Al-though belief in the Gadarene swine tale was not necessary to dogma, Wace had described himself, nevertheless, as accepting it. Huxley aims a number of jibes at the clergyman for his gul-libility. But "Agnosticism: A Rejoinder" is just a little too per-sonal and a bit too discourteous for comfort.

Wace, who was predictably unimpressed by Huxley's argu-ment, responded the following month; and Huxley answered in the *Nineteenth Century* for June, 1889. By this time, how-ever, neither antagonist had anything to add to his original ar-gument. Huxley, after completing his final article, referred to it as being "as full of malice as an egg is of meat."[32] This de-scription could also be extended to the three "Agnosticism" es-says and to describe one of their salient weaknesses. Huxley, too bluntly critical of Christianity and too inhospitable to the point of view of his antagonist, refuses to concede the benefits that have accrued from Christian teaching and concentrates exclusively on its absurdities. Moreover, his mood is petulant and impatient, and his tone too often harsh and biting.[33]

VI *Evaluation*

In these polemics centering on theological questions it is necessary to distinguish between Huxley "the Bishop eater" and Huxley the serious biblical critic. In his attempts to bring the discoveries of science to bear upon the Bible—as he did in "Hasiadra's Adventure" and "The Evolution of Theology"— Huxley was at his best. These articles reflect the thinking of such distinguished Continental biblical critics as Ernest Renan, F. C. Baur, David Strauss, and Édouard Reuss. Most of his other controversial writings, however, suffer from too much repetition and elementary exposition and from the necessity to correct the "errors" of his antagonists. He is too frequently occupied with the fundamentals to deliver the balanced, lucid account of the conflict between scientific and biblical cosmogonies that the question certainly warranted. This characteristic is doubly unfortunate because these essays were widely read in their day, an indication that the public felt that the subject was of great importance.[34]

In the last analysis, however, such pitfalls were probably unavoidable. Controversial writing is inevitably concerned with the pursuit of victory rather than truth, and most seasoned warriors concede that might and right do not necessarily go together. On occasion Huxley was not above employing the art of rhetoric to achieve his own ends, and his *ad hominem* attacks could be quite cruel. On other occasions he was not above stretching the truth or taking refuge behind certain views to which he might not have lent his support under other circumstances. Critics of Huxley have commented on these tendencies in an effort to demonstrate that he did not always hold the cause of truth as his highest allegiance. Houston Peterson, for one, has persuasively argued that Huxley's defense of his philosophical position—his agnosticism—contradicts itself at many points.[35]

Paul Elmer More in a penetrating but highly unsympathetic essay in *The Drift of Romanticism* also charges Huxley with being so flexible in his skepticism that he was constantly altering his intellectual position to suit the needs of the moment.[36]

More's point is well taken, but his evaluation of Huxley as "one of the master sophists of his age" is misleading; for it leaves the impression that Huxley was engaged consciously in a campaign to mislead the public—an evaluation that does not fit the other facts of Huxley's career. Perhaps the worst that can be said of Huxley is that he changed his ground out of a reluctance to be bested in controversy, not out of a conscious desire to deceive.

Reviewing his career in 1892, Huxley anticipated many of these criticisms concerning his activities in the arena of controversy. In his Prologue to Controverted Questions he made the following comment on polemical writing:

It is often useful, sometimes necessary, and always more or less of an evil. It is useful when it attracts attention to topics which might otherwise be neglected; and when as does sometimes happen, those who come to see a contest remain to think. It is necessary when the interests of truth and of justice are at stake. It is an evil, in so far as controversy always tends to degenerate into quarreling, to swerve from the great issue of what is right to the very small question of who is right and who is wrong.[37]

CHAPTER 7

Politics and Theology

I N April, 1888, Huxley was finally able to complete a task that he had been working on for years—the Darwin obituary for the Royal Society. The notice laid particular stress on Darwin's life-long dedication to science and scientific reasoning, his careful observation of nature, and his high moral character. The necessity to review the life of the author of the *Origin* only made Huxley's admiration for Darwin the greater. "I am getting sick and tired of all the 'paper philosophers,' " he told a friend, "who are trying to stand on Darwin's shoulders and look bigger than he is, when in point of real knowledge they are not fit to black his shoes."[1]

Excursions to Switzerland were now a summer ritual, but his trip of 1888 was delayed for a number of weeks by ill health. On his return, improved by the Alpine air but far from cured, he was buoyed by the news that he had been awarded the highest honor of the Royal Society, the Copley Medal. The recipient the previous year had been Sir Joseph Hooker, and in 1864 the Copley had been given to Darwin. In granting Darwin the award, however, the President of the Society had been at pains to stress that it was for work exclusive of the *Origin of Species*. But the climate of opinion had decidedly altered in the intervening quarter of a century, and no such reservations attached to either the case of Huxley or Hooker. Hooker had, of course, like Huxley, spent a number of years at sea as a young man. In a letter to his friend Huxley speaks of their having "a masonic bond in early life. I have always felt I owed a great deal to my acquaintance with the realities of things gained in the old *Rattlesnake*."[2] Huxley never forgot the impression the cruise had made on him.

I *Rousseau and George*

During the early months of 1889 Huxley was chiefly employed with the "agnosticism" articles. They were largely composed at Eastbourne, where he was now overseeing the construction of a new home. In November, however, his interest in the progress of the building was distracted by a flurry of letters to the London *Times.* The result was that he now emerged in a new role: the political scientist. The question that had engaged the paper's correspondents concerned the legitimacy of private property. Two of the authorities cited were revolutionaries, Jean Jacques Rousseau and Henry George. George, of course, was the American political economist who advocated a scheme of land reform whereby government expenses would be raised by a Single Tax. There was nothing Huxley disliked quite so much as glib and facile spokesmen for revolution, and he entered the fray with a letter on November 12th, then followed it with two more within a week. Knowles asked Huxley for an article, and Huxley responded with "The Natural Inequality of Men" (*Nineteenth Century,* January, 1890), the first of four which he wrote for the periodical that year.

This article was directed primarily at workingmen. Huxley had intended to republish it as part of a series of pamphlets similar to *The Causes of the Phenomena of Organic Nature,* which he had used to popularize the ideas of Darwin forty years before; but the plan was never implemented. "The Natural Inequality of Men"[3] is an attack on the ideas of Rousseau—chiefly on his theories concerning private property. Huxley did not feel Rousseau's ideas could ever have in England anything like the influence they had in France, nor did he think England was susceptible to the possibility of a revolution; but he did feel that, given wide currency, Rousseau's ideas could have a mischievous effect, especially since his works were at the time being widely read by workingmen.

Huxley offers Rousseau as the very archetype of the thinker who feels that all human suffering can be attributed to the indifference of society toward the needs of the individual. What gave his ideas a certain amount of currency even among intelligent men, Huxley suggests, is that he developed them from first principles that were superficially plausible—first principles not unlike those of Hobbes and Locke. Rousseau had advanced the notion that human unhappiness has two causes: the ownership of private property, and the inequality of social status that obtains in all human society. Huxley counters with an argument in which he maintains that political inequality follows directly from natural inequality. Such inequality is inevitable because of the inequality of natural faculties among men; differences in natural ability are inherent, are not necessarily to be deplored, and are apparent even among very young children.

In his next two articles Huxley extended his attack on would-be fomenters of revolution to include Henry George. "Did you ever read Henry George's book 'Progress and Poverty'?" he asked Knowles. "It is more damnder [sic] nonsense than poor Rousseau's blether."[4] In his first essay Huxley had countered Rousseau's argument for communal property ownership with one which based right of ownership on such pragmatic considerations as force. In attacking George's labor theory of value (that possession should result directly from labor), he countered with an argument no less pragmatic: ownership of property is legitimate so long as the ownership is acquired through means sanctioned by the society itself.

Huxley met the arguments of the arch revolutionaries with ones no less arch in their conservatism: as far as "natural rights" are concerned, they are so much humbug. In theory, perhaps, men are born with a natural right to freedom; but, as members of a polity, they agree to limits upon this freedom. Which liberties men must forego depends on the nature of the particular society to which they belong. A man makes the best agreement for his services that he can under prevailing conditions; and, Huxley implies, his rewards are commensurate with his abilities. The principle underlying Huxley's argument is that any society, no matter how bad, is better than none. The "natural rights" theory is nothing more than "reasoned savagery, with an unmitigated selfishness, incompatible with social existence."[5]

"Capital—Mother of Labour"[6] is a continuation of his attack on *Progress and Poverty*—chiefly on George's definitions of such terms as "labor," "capital," "wealth," "wages," and "value." But this article also shows why Huxley was so unsympathetic to the Socialist movements of the nineteenth century. Contrary to the Marxists and the Fabians, who believed labor and capital to be antagonistic, Huxley describes them as allies. Capital is, in fact, a "necessary antecedent of labor and it furnishes the materials on which labor is employed."

Huxley concluded his excursion into political science with "Government: Anarchy or Regimentation."[7] This article shows that Huxley's political theory had not altered very much since 1871, when the passage of the Education Act had led him to comment on the role of the government in the affairs of the individual. At that time Huxley had approved of the government's decision to administer elementary education and had urged that it regulate commerce, sanitation, and even the arts and sciences. In reply to the argument that government involvement with private enterprise could establish a dangerous precedent, he exhibited an almost sublime confidence in the good judgment of legislators, saying they are generally able to discern "when state interference has been carried far enough." This argument is essentially that of the "Government" essay, which has a decidedly twentieth-century ring in its thought and its terminology. Huxley carefully examines the place of the individual in relation to the group, and the probable consequences of too much and too little government. The greatest political problem, he concludes, is overpopulation—a dilemma for which he offers no solution.

II *Political and Social Views; the Eyre Controversy*

Over the course of his career, Huxley seldom made public statements on political questions; but his private correspondence frequently alludes to politics. Huxley's involvement with education and with the administrative aspects of British science made it inevitable that he eventually be requested to stand for Parliament. He was, in fact, asked on a number of occasions but always refused on the same grounds that had prompted him to refrain from making public statements of a political nature: he was anxious to remain above partisan politics. Despite his close association with Darwin, it is not unlikely—considering the ease with which Huxley was elected to the London School Board—that he would have made a fair showing at the polls. But, since he considered science as a calling superior to all others and himself as one of its chief spokesmen, he was not anxious to become associated with any one political cause. Nevertheless, while he was not doctrinaire in his views, Huxley's political outlook was liberal and democratic.

Nowhere is his liberalism more apparent than in his long, persistent campaign to bring the truths of science to the working classes. Much of this effort expended on behalf of English workingmen was inspired by a deeply felt sympathy for them and was far more than lip service paid to an abstract principle. "I am a plebian and stand by my order," he once declared; and the lectures he delivered at the South London Workingmen's College were always prepared with care and were a source of particular satisfaction to him.

Huxley was not possessed by the animosity toward aristocratic institutions that so often marks democratic reformers, but he felt that a social organization based on a rigid caste system could only be harmful for all of society. In "Administrative Nihilism"[8] he spoke out forcefully against the "social corks" which tend to keep afloat so many bunglers and incompetents whose only claim to eminence was that they happened to be well-born. Education and opportunities for self-improvement should be available to all citizens, Huxley felt; and he was confident that superior men would make the most of them. The benefits would accrue not only to them as individuals but to society as a whole; for, as he said in the same essay, the higher the stage of civilization, "the less possible is it for any one man to do a wrong thing without interfering more or less, with the freedom of all his fellow citizens." Huxley, in fact, recognized that misery and discontent among large segments of the population constituted a very serious threat to society; and he was always made uneasy by the opulence and the poverty that existed in close proximity. On a visit to Liverpool he did not conceal the shock he felt at the sight of "unwashed, unkempt brutal people side by side with indications of the greatest refinement and the greatest luxury."[9]

These flagrant examples of inequality, he felt, were giving impetus to the many Socialist movements then stirring Europe and the United States. Not a Socialist himself and not particularly sympathetic to the reasoning employed by Socialists to justify their cause, he nevertheless recognized that these movements were supported by many able and determined men and that their aims were legitimate. At the same time, however, he tended to be suspicious of democratic movements which give too much power to the masses. For this reason he opposed the movement for Irish independence; for the Irish, a politically naïve, agricultural people, would be, he frankly thought, "incapable of governing themselves." Huxley did not undervalue the perquisites of democratic society, and he naturally placed a high value on freedom of expression and thought. He had sense enough to know that if he had been defending the theories of Galileo, rather than those of Darwin, he doubtless would have ended his career as the nameless victim of some obscure Torquemada. In the last analysis, however, he considered inequality among men to be a fact of life; the business of society should be to permit responsible, superior men places which they had earned through their achievement.

Just as Huxley strongly opposed independence for Ireland, so did he have somewhat similar views toward British rule in India. Though he recognized that the movements of the times favored Indian independence, he felt that, as long as England chose to maintain the empire there, it should be done, when necessary, by force. Exactly what Huxley understood by "force," however, is not entirely clear. That he did not mean brutality is made plain by the stand he took in the Eyre controversy, a colonial scandal which rocked England late in 1865.

Feeling in England ran high as a result of the severity with which Edward John Eyre, Governor of Jamaica, put down a Negro revolution in the colony. In the process of squashing the revolt, one of the leaders was hanged without benefit of a trial on direct orders of the governor. In England the Jamaica Committee was immediately formed by John Stuart Mill, who wanted Eyre brought to trial on charges of murder. Lyell, Spencer, Darwin, and Huxley gave their support to Mill; but a no less eminent group—Tyndall, Carlyle, Charles Kingsley, and Hooker—rallied in Eyre's defense. Editorial writers up and down the land printed the views of their publishers. When the *Pall Mall Gazette* chided Darwin and Huxley for the "sympathetic recognition" they extended to Britain's colonial subjects, Huxley immediately sent a letter of explanation in which he maintained that he had not acted out of feelings of sympathy but from a "deeply rooted objection to this method of killing people—and the act itself appears to me to be so frightful a precedent that I desire to see it stigmatised by the highest authority as a crime."[10]

Efforts by the committee to have Eyre brought to trial failed, however; he was suspended and recalled, but never tried.

The affair came close to severing Huxley's friendship with Tyndall, who had rallied to Eyre's support chiefly out of admiration for Carlyle. Huxley had denounced the pro-Eyre faction as a pack of "hero-worshippers." Before matters reached a violent stage, however, Tyndall explained his side of the question to Huxley. He referred to Huxley's letter to the *Pall Mall Gazette* as "a source of pain more keen than ... words are likely to make you aware of." "If you and I are strong enough and wise enough," Huxley wrote back, "we shall be able to ... preserve that love for one another which I value as one of the good things on my life."[11] The friendship survived.

III *Second Controversy with Gladstone*

No sooner had Huxley concluded his foray into politics than he found himself once more in the thick of a theological dispute. In the fall of 1890, William Gladstone, then out of office, had the leisure to collect his writings on religion into one volume, which he called *The Impregnable Rock of Holy Scripture* (Huxley later described the title as "defiant"). Gladstone summarized the thoughts contained in the book in a concluding essay; and, needless to add, this contribution contained nothing that was new or startling. He reasserted the relevance of Christian teaching to the modern world, declared there was nothing in Christian dogma which contradicted the findings of science, and dismissed philosophical skepticism as merely one of the transient "negative tendencies of the day."

Apparently, however, Gladstone had been observing Huxley's exchange with Principal Wace with some attention; for he included in his conclusion a comment on a statement of Huxley's contained in "Agnosticism" where Huxley had referred to the destruction of the herd of pigs as a "misdemeanor of evil example." Gladstone inferred from this remark that Huxley had directed a criticism at the character of Jesus. "So then," Gladstone wrote, "after eighteen centuries of worship offered to Our

Lord . . . it has been reserved to a scientific inquirer to discover that He was no better than a lawbreaker and an evil doer."[12] But Huxley's point had been that belief in the Gospels was principally a question of testimony, and he had stated that he was skeptical of the veracity of the story. Gladstone had clearly missed the implications of Huxley's essay, and he had compounded his original error by offering the opinion that Jesus was justified in destroying the pigs since Gadara was a Jewish city and keeping swine was in violation of Jewish law.

The title of Huxley's rejoinder, "The Keepers of the Herd of Swine,"[13] conveys the main drift of the contents. The swineherds were not, after all, bound by Jewish law; and, amid a parade of authorities, Huxley demonstrates that Gadara was a Hellenic city. But this peg was rather an insubstantial one on which to hang a long essay, despite the impressiveness of Huxley's biblical scholarship. It was becoming abundantly plain that, the longer Huxley fought, the more trivial were the issues. When Gladstone replied in the *Nineteenth Century* for February, 1891, and defended his earlier assertions, Huxley responded with an article in which he directed his criticism at Gladstone rather than at his opinions.

"Mr. Gladstone's Controversial Methods,"[14] Huxley's final contribution in his prolonged debate with Gladstone, is largely an attack on Gladstone and his career as a politician. Huxley's opinion of politicians, of course, had never been very high. If a man had any decency of character or a brain, Huxley felt, a political career was a sure way of destroying it. "I am inclined to think" he wrote to Knowles in 1895, "that the practice of the methods of political leaders destroys their intelligence for all serious purposes."[15]

Huxley employed this essay as an occasion for criticizing Gladstone and the methods he had used to bring himself to his high place in the world. The following passage, for example, is not only a back-handed slap at the ways political leaders advance themselves, it is also a statement of the superiority of science as a career to politics. A political leader, Huxley suggests, should not stray from his own bailiwick; for, "he is apt to forget that he will be judged by . . . people, on whom rhetorical artifices have long ceased to take effect; and to whom mere dexterity in putting together cleverly ambiguous phrases, and even the great art of offensive misrepresentation, are unspeakably wearisome."

The Huxley-Gladstone debates are too heavily saturated with the personalities of the participants to be of any great appeal to twentieth-century readers. At the time, many Englishmen were amused by the dispute; but to others it hardly seemed that the argument warranted such quantities of space in one of the nation's most eminent periodicals. Indeed, Huxley was sensitive to the criticism that he and Gladstone were expending a good deal of energy and magazine space on trivial and prosaic questions. He concluded the debate by trying to invest the controversy with a larger significance—but without much success. He said that it was "degrading" that men of the nineteenth century should support the demonology of men of the first century, and restated his belief that "behind the question of the acceptance of the doctrines of heathen demonology ... there lies the question of the credibility of the Gospels."

This debate seems quite dated today; and, though the questions have yet to be resolved, they have become considerably altered in the intervening years. Literal interpretations of the Bible today are advanced almost exclusively by fundamentalists; and public men, for all their frequent references to the deity in political oratory, are generally reluctant to engage in the kind of argument which Gladstone undertook—although going back four decades one can point to the very obvious exception of William Jennings Bryan.

IV Theologian Manqué?

During the fall of 1890 Huxley also became involved in another, somewhat peculiar, dispute with the Salvation Army. Earlier in the year General William Booth had published *In Darkest England,* in which he had advanced a ten-point program of reform to cure the country's ills. The plan received wide support and was heavily subscribed. A lady about to donate one thousand pounds decided at the last minute to consult Huxley on the matter. When Huxley read the book, examined the aims and practices of the army and, concluding that the organization constituted a national threat, he made his views public on December 1 in a letter to the *Times.* Evidently Huxley regarded

Booth as a thinker with habits of mind similar to those of Henry George—one who attributed all human ills to an unsympathetic society and whose premises could lead only to anarchic individualism or autocratic Socialism. And the fact that the scheme had a theological exterior did not endear it to Huxley. Such programs, he declares, can succeed only when they attack corruption at "its ultimate source—namely, the motives of the individual man."[16]

Naturally, the letter brought rejoinders to which Huxley had to reply; all told, he wrote twelve letters during January and February. Huxley had not expected the controversy to become so drawn out, and he soon became aware of the ultimate futility of his campaign. In a letter to his son he humbly asks him not to regard the controversy as "the advance of a forlorn hope."[17] The Salvation Army, of course, continued to prosper; and General Booth was an honored guest at the coronation in 1902 of Edward VII.

It is likely that Huxley saw in the muscular and martial Christianity of the Salvation Army many resemblances to the fundamentalism on which he had been reared as a boy and which he had so heartily detested in later years. Born in 1825, Huxley entered the world during one of the more undistinguished decades of the nineteenth century. This particular period in English history is today largely remembered, when remembered at all, for the fact that a squalid and shapeless religious fundamentalism had inexplicably gripped the population and was spreading throughout the land like a contagious disease.

The Evangelical Revival, as the movement was called, ran its feverish course and ultimately gave way in the following decade to its direct antithesis in the sophisticated and highly intellectual Oxford movement. Nevertheless, Huxley's first brush with theology and theologians took place during the 1830's when, as he recalled in the "Prologue" to *Controverted Questions*, "the evangelical flood had a little abated and the tops of certain mountains were soon to appear, chiefly in the neighborhood of Oxford; but when nevertheless ... church and chapel alike proclaimed, as the oracles of God, the crude assumptions of the worst informed and, in natural sequence, the most presumptuously bigoted, of all theological schools."[18]

Unfortunately for the young Huxley, the evangelical flood had not yet "abated" to the point where it precluded clerical tirades generously laced with fire, brimstone, and dark promises of an eternity of flames as the consequence for failure to heed Divine precepts. A severe and intolerant religious indoctrination of this type is guaranteed to have one of two effects on a strong-minded individual: either he capitulates entirely to authority and becomes a fanatical disciple, or he becomes eternally resentful of the advantage taken of him and becomes contumacious toward such authority.

The second alternative was clearly the result of Huxley's early encounter with Evangelical Christianity. How lasting were the effects of this painful experience is to be seen six decades later when he recalled the experience in terms he might have employed to describe at a comparable age having been shanghaied on a Roman galley:

In accordance with promises made on my behalf, but certainly without my authorisation, I was very early taken to hear "sermons in the vulgar tongue." And vulgar enough often was the tongue in which some preacher, ignorant alike of literature, of history, of science, and even of theology, outside that patronised by his own narrow school, poured forth, from the safe entrenchment of the pulpit, invectives against those who deviated from the notion of orthodoxy. . . . I suppose that, out of a thousand of my contemporaries, nine hundred, at least, had their minds systematically warped and poisoned, in the name of the God of truth, by like discipline.[19]

Huxley never made any attempt to conceal the joy he derived from making bishops look like humbugs, and in later years he derived equal relish from exposing theology to common sense. He testified that his controversy with Gladstone succeeded in restoring his liver juices to their normal flow and returned him to a state of good health that he had not enjoyed for years. It is not necessary to have a deep knowledge of Freudian psychology to make the connection between these pursuits and Huxley's early sufferings at the hands of ecclesiastics; Huxley, indeed, admitted as much many times himself. "It is a sort of crib biting," he wrote of his theological warfare on one occasion.

This is not to say that, had Huxley been brought up in a neutral atmosphere, he would have been a conventional thinker or a regular churchgoer. Nor is it to say that he under any circumstances would have been able to refrain from making fun of Archbishop Manning at the meetings of the Metaphysical Society or, given such a great opportunity, would ever have been able to forego the chance to deflate the pretensions of Bishop Wilberforce. Huxley's differences with such men went far deeper than their respective convictions on theology. There is a chance, however, that he would have been able to remain indifferent to the theological speculations of Gladstone—a controversy, the result of which was a good deal of heat but little light—and to certain clerical tirades against science which moved him to urge laymen to cease regarding "the clergy ... when in the pulpit, as a sort of chartered libertines, whose divagations are not to be taken seriously."[20]

Yet, when he was not forced to be the gladiator and was free to write on theology as he pleased, Huxley could be wonderfully illuminating and ingenious. His own contemporaries—with the exception of the most liberal—were not always prepared for the devastating biblical criticism which he practiced in such articles as *Hasiadra's Adventure,* where he brought a superb knowledge of Babylonian mythology and geological conditions in the Holy Land to cast doubt on the literal truth of the biblical account of the deluge.[21] The great "Controverted Question" of the day, Huxley said, was how far supernature and nature were to go in claiming the attentions of man; and he did not conceal his own inclination to give all the attentions of men to the province of nature. It was, in fact, this supreme rationalism which even the most broadminded came to deplore because to deprive the Bible of its theological underpinnings, they feared, would result in moral chaos, the unique position enjoyed by the Bible giving it an almost unequalled claim upon the attentions and respect of men.

V *Evolution of Theology*

Huxley's most incisive thoughts on theological questions are contained in "Evolution of Theology" (1886),[22] in which he brought the findings of anthropology to bear on matters of theology and morality, and in which he anticipated Frazer's *The*

Golden Bough, one of the most important and influential books of the early twentieth century. The essay represents Huxley at his most scientific (and therefore at his most irreligious), and he self-consciously prefaced the work with a warning to the pious not to read it if they were not prepared for the thoughts it contained.

According to Huxley, morality predates theology, and had its beginning with society itself. With the dawn of society, men realized that certain rules would have to be observed in order to gain the advantages of social existence. Only with the passage of time, as rules of morality became more complex, did men begin to feel the urge to break them. At this time a higher authority for the existence of laws was sought; and, "in the absence of a clear apprehension of the natural sanction of these rules," Huxley writes, "a supernatural sanction was assumed. . . . Religion, at first independent of morality, gradually took morality under its protection; and the supernaturalists have ever since tried to persuade mankind that the existence of ethics is bound up with that of supernaturalism."

Despite the importance of this essay, the fact is inescapable that the time Huxley spent in theological disputation, by and large, could have been put to better use; and his writings on the subject—despite their ingenuity, strength of conviction, and pellucidity of statement—did not succeed in wielding nearly as much influence as did those on science and education. They were certainly not responsible for causing as much intellectual ferment or general soul-searching as were those of Newman or even Matthew Arnold.

So far as Newman was concerned, Huxley had a certain reluctant admiration for him; but, as William Irvine has observed, he did not understand him—nor did he want to do so. Huxley felt, perhaps, that Newman's theology was infinitely superior to that of the Evangelical churchmen; but, since Newman reasoned from premises Huxley considered erroneous, Huxley was never able to extend him a sympathetic hearing. His references to Newman in his correspondence are, in fact, frequently quite harsh. "I have been reading some of his works," he writes to Knowles in 1889, "and I understand now why Kingsley accused him of growing dishonesty. After an hour or two of him I begin to lose sight of the distinction between truth and falsehood."[23] Huxley's lack of an open mind was one of his more glaring defects for, in the last analysis, he had much in common with men such as Newman and the Bishop of Peterborough. And, after moving to Eastbourne in 1890, he enjoyed a most convivial relationship with Newman's articulate disciple Wilfred Ward.

Huxley's manner and attitudes, in fact, were themselves somewhat ecclesiastical. In his "Autobiography" Huxley even recalled how, as a young boy, he once turned his pinafore around to resemble a surplice and preached a sermon in the manner of the local vicar. "That," he writes, "is the earliest indication I can call to mind of the strong clerical affinities which my friend Mr. Herbert Spencer has always ascribed to me, though I fancy they have for the most part remained in the latent state." Spencer, however, was only one of many who saw in Huxley the qualities of a theologian *manqué*, and in 1870 his cocksure manner and his practice of handing down opinions *ex cathedra* inspired R. H. Hutton, who came to know Huxley well through the Metaphysical Society, to write an article for the *Spectator* entitled "Pope Huxley."

Huxley's theological opinions seem to have crystallized while he was still in his early twenties, and they remained unchanged until his death. The journal he kept on board the *Rattlesnake* contains an entry in which he speaks of metaphysics being "one wild whirl," and it is probable that at about this time he abandoned the theological beliefs to which he had subscribed during his childhood and adolescence. Huxley had taken an "agnostic" view of supernatural phenomena two decades prior to coining the word.

Huxley's position in respect to metaphysics was widely misunderstood in his own day, but it was really quite simple. All conclusions concerning the existence of a supernature, he felt, were not subject to verification so he would neither accept nor reject their existence. Huxley's ethical agnosticism was a puzzle to many contemporaries, and his vigorous campaign on behalf of Darwin, along with such literary contributions as *Man's Place in Nature* and "The Physical Basis of Life," had earned for him the reputation of a godless materialist even before he turned his attention to metaphysics proper. Afterwards, it was not uncommon for men of orthodox views to make him the target of such harsh names as "materialist," "infidel," and "skeptic"; and some, not content with mere namecalling, darkly hinted that Professor Huxley's godless philosophy was an attempted justification for what was essentially a libertarian existence. Although such charges might not have been groundless in the case of many another eminent Victorian, they could not be justified in respect to Huxley. His one vice was smoking too much; his name remains entirely free of any kind of scandal.

Huxley the man—by his loyalty to his friends, his devotion to his family, his seemingly inexhaustible capacity for work, and the unselfishness with which he gave of his time to public service —set an example for those who knew him in his own day and for countless thousands of men of succeeding generations. He actually became a model for men who, sharing his skepticism of theology and abhorrence of humbug, were neverthless anxious to contribute to the general welfare and were, withal, content to allow their personal reputations to rest on nothing other than solid achievement. Significantly, H. G. Wells, who studied only briefly with Huxley at South Kensington, used to describe himself in later years as "one of Huxley's men." Huxley had a unique gift for inspiring loyalty and admiration.

Huxley wrote to Charles Kingsley in 1860 that "*Sartor Resartus* led me to know that a deep sense of religion was compatible with the entire absence of theology."[24] Huxley's differences with Christian ecclesiastics were almost without exception academic, centering generally on abstruse points of theology; on the essentials there was no quarrel. "I have a great respect for the Nazarenism of Jesus," Huxley declared in 1892. "But the only religion that appeals to me is prophetic Judaism. Add to it something from the best Stoics and something from Spinoza and something from Goethe, and there is a religion for men."[25]

Throughout his entire life Huxley continued to think of Holy Writ as a source not only of poetical but of practical wisdom, and his only reservations concerned the claims made for it by Christians who believed it was inspired directly by God which, as he wrote in the "Prologue" to *Controverted Questions*, were "pretensions to infallibility set up, not by the ancient Hebrew writings themselves, but by the ecclesiastical champions and friends from whom they may well pray to be delivered." In 1870 in his School Boards essay Huxley had delivered a strong opinion in favor of Bible reading in the public schools, and the fact that he reprinted this section of his essay in 1892 is evidence that he continued to hold his esteem for Holy Writ to the end of his life.

The skepticism of Huxley, like that of Hume, was an intellectual ideal; however, as a guide to practical living it was of small value. There was a wide gulf between the intellectual precepts of Huxley and his personal ethics. In the laboratory, nothing, he felt, should be taken for granted; no possibility should be excluded until it had been disproved through experiment. In his own life, however, he was no experimenter; he was conservative in politics and lived by traditional precepts of morality. In this respect too he resembled Hume, whose very name struck horror in the breasts of the orthodox, but who was revered by his friends and known among them as "*le bon* David." Adam Smith, a close friend of Hume, even spoke of him "as approaching as nearly to the idea of a perfectly wise and virtuous man as perhaps the nature of human frailty will permit."

Their remoteness from everyday life explains in part why Huxley's writings on theology failed to have much impact on the public. His differences with orthodox churchmen turned on abstract and remote theological points such as the value of miracles, and for this reason they did not appeal much to the public at large. The stated aims of such lectures were to show that, as history, the Bible did not meet the standards of veracity which one requires from other historical works and, ultimately, to place a check on the tendency toward bibliolatry. But bibliolatry was already under fire from within the church, for the authors of *Essays and Reviews* and Bishop Colenso had launched their own attacks three decades before, and the Broad Churchmen were already a powerful faction within the Church of England. Huxley's differences with ecclesiastics frequently were not so great as he himself imagined them to be, and his attacks were only more extreme than those that had their source within the church itself.

CHAPTER 8

Last Years

1891 dawned with Huxley comfortably settled in his new home in Eastbourne. Some researches into his ancestry which he conducted at this time traced his family back to Cheshire during the reign of Richard I; and this discovery led him to christen his new home "Hodeslea," an approximation of the Anglo-Saxon form of his surname. Forty years earlier Huxley had spoken of London as "the place—the center of the world"; but since he was having some difficulty with his lungs, Huxley was now very much inclined to go along with Darwin who considered the city to be a "vile and smokey place."

It was inevitable in any case that Huxley forego many of the activities of the city, and it was not long before he adjusted to the slower pace of the seashore. The salt air of the coast seems to have soothed his spirit as well as his body; for, after completing his second dispute with Gladstone, he remained away from controversy for the balance of 1891 and for most of 1892. Life was, on the whole, far more leisurely than he had dreamed it ever could be. Always a prompt letter writer, he sometimes allowed correspondence to lie unanswered for weeks at a time.

His rule was to take an eight o'clock breakfast, spend an hour and a half at his writing desk, and then indulge his latest interest—his garden. After an afternoon walk, he would return to his study, have dinner, and spend the evening reading philosophy, history, and novels. But there is ample evidence that he remained *au courant* with the latest scientific developments. He closely followed Louis Robinson's investigations into the simian characteristics of newborn children; evinced excited interest in the work of William Bateson, who had recently published his findings on variations; and in 1895 he commented to Hooker on the discovery by Eugène DuBois in Borneo of *Pithe-*

canthropus erectus, one of the most significant fossil finds of the last century.

Much of 1891 was devoted to the collection of his controversial articles into one volume and to the composition of a long prologue. As he grew older, Huxley took more and more care with his writing. It was now his rule to revise an essay as many as five or six times before sending it to the printer. He described his "Prologue" to *Controverted Questions* as having "cost more time and pains than any equal number of pages I have ever written."[1]

I *"An Apologetic Irenicon"*

When the volume appeared the following year, it occasioned a controversy with a longtime friendly enemy, Frederic Harrison. Huxley's dislike for the ideas of Harrison went back almost a quarter of a century. Unlike Gladstone and the Duke of Argyll, however, Harrison never stood still long enough for Huxley to annihilate him. Educated for the bar at Wadham College, Oxford, Harrison was a prolific writer, a distinguished essayist and biographer of, among others, Cromwell, Ruskin, and Chatham. But it was his connection with Positivism, of which he was a leader, that brought him into conflict with Huxley. One of the founders of *The Positivist Review,* he tirelessly advocated the views of Comte in numerous articles and lectures; and these activities moved Huxley to label him (in "An Apologetic Irenicon") as the "plenipotentiary of latter-day Positivism."

Indeed, for many years Harrison was so saturated with the theories of Comte he was unable to write on any subject without including somewhere a paean to the Frenchman. In fact, shortly after Huxley's disagreement with Congreve, Harrison wrote an article titled "The Positivist Problem" (*Fortnightly,* November, 1869) in which he studiously omitted all mention of Huxley; and, all things considered, the most surprising aspect of the Huxley-Harrison debate was that it did not occur twenty years earlier.

Huxley was first moved to reply to an allegation of Harrison's in his essay on "Agnosticism." Harrison had written an article in which he predicted a short future for the agnostic movement

—calling it "a stage in the evolution of religion, an entirely negative stage ... with no relation to things social at all." Huxley professed astonishment that a man of Harrison's intellect and education could have made such a superficial evaluation of agnosticism. Huxley repeated his assertion that agnosticism was no kind of formal religious faith; and, far from being an aberration of a small band of physicists, as Harrison hd suggested, it was a logical result of historical forces. It was, he felt, "the only religion which will prove itself to be unassailably acceptable so long as the human race endures."

But Huxley had no illusions about the power of widespread enlightenment to alter the condition of mankind. Huxley's knowledge of anthropology made it impossible for him to overlook man's animal origins. Man, Huxley says, "is a brute, only more intelligent than the other brutes.... He attains a certain degree of physical comfort ... in such favorable situations as the plains of Mesopotamia or Egypt, and then, for thousands and thousands of years, struggles with varying fortunes, attended by infinite wickedness, bloodshed, and misery to maintain himself at this point against the greed and the ambition of his fellow men."[2]

Huxley's explanation did not permanently silence Harrison. In a review of Huxley's book *Essays on Some Controverted Questions* in the *Fortnightly* (1892), Harrison had repeated many of his earlier assertions. Among other statements, he had said again that agnosticism was a "negative stage in the evolution of religion." He was, moreover, critical of Huxley's book because it did not contain any "positive assurance as to a moral Providence, as to the will or nature of any Supreme Power or Force, as to the state of man or any part of man after death, as to the nature of sin, or as to any punishment or reward beyond those of this life."

When Huxley replied in "An Apologetic Irenicon" (*Fortnightly*, November, 1892), he eloquently affirmed his belief in the rationality and order of the universe. Providence, he says, is "the total exclusion of chance from a place even in the most insignificant corner of Nature." As for the findings of Darwin, he declares that they do not provide the foundation for an ethical system. There can be no "ethics of evolution" because there is no necessary connection between the "fittest" and the ethically best. "The fittest which survives in the struggle for existence," he declares dramatically, "may be, and often is, the ethically worst."

In Huxley's early essays there is a good deal of stoicism; but, toward the end of his life, this point of view evolved toward something very close to pessimism. He would have been the first to deny it ("If the optimism of Leibnitz is a foolish though pleasant dream, the pessimism of Schopenhauer is a nightmare, the more foolish because of its hideousness,"[3] he wrote in 1888); but there is no escaping that his view became increasingly fatalistic.

Nor could he derive any consolation from the Christian concept of eternal life, for "if a genuine, not merely subjective immortality awaits us, I conceive that, without some such change as that depicted in the fifteenth chapter of the Second Epistle to the Corinthians, immortality must be eternal misery." Naturally, he did not expect that these ideas would be received with anything like enthusiasm by his contemporaries. "As in the past, so, I fear," he concludes, "through a very long future, the multitude will continue to turn to those who ... will offer mental peace where there is no peace; and lap it in the luxury of pleasant delusions." "An Apologetic Irenicon" clearly foreshadows his Romanes essay, which he later delivered at Oxford University.

II   *The Game Was Worth the Candle*

Huxley was, of course, a gregarious man. A witty and ready speaker, he greatly enjoyed the fellowship provided by scientific organizations and groups like the Metaphysical Society; and he was, in addition, a member of a number of clubs, including the Athenaeum. The society of which he was most fond, however, was the X Club, a select group of Royal Society members which ran English science. Founded in 1864, it counted among its members Spencer; Tyndall; and John Lubbock, the anthropologist. The little society of nine members met for dinner before the monthly meetings of the Royal Society and endured until 1892. However, with the death in February of that year of Thomas Hirst, the mathematician, membership fell off to six;

and, of those remaining, five now lived outside London. When the club convened for its two hundred and fortieth meeting in March, the thought that must have been in the minds of all the members was left unspoken: the little group that had unofficially looked after the affairs of the Royal Society for three decades had convened for the last time. The leadership of English science had passed on to another generation.

Honors continued to come to Huxley. In May he was asked if he would be willing to deliver the second annual Romanes lecture at Oxford the following year. Regarding the occasion as a splendid opportunity to address himself to a subject which he had been pondering for thirty years—the impact of Darwinism on morality—he immediately, or almost immediately, announced his acceptance: delivery of the address was to depend on the state of his health. The university authorities accepted the condition, and the address was duly scheduled for the following May. The title of the address was "Evolution and Ethics."

In August he was granted admission to the Privy Council. "If I had been offered to be made a police constable, I could not have been more flabbergasted,"[4] Huxley told Hooker. He was conveyed to the palace in an ornately decorated carriage where, resplendent in court dress with sword and scabbard, he took part in the ancient ritual which included kneeling to kiss the hand of the queen. "What a quaint ceremony it is!"[5] he remarked afterward. The effect of the exertion was that he was laid up for a week, but he felt the inconvenience to have been well worth the effort.

In October, Huxley was informed of the death of Tennyson. Huxley first became acquainted with the poet laureate at the meetings of the Metaphysical Society, and he had a high regard for him both as a man and as a poet. Tennyson, according to Huxley, was "the first poet since Lucretius who has understood the drift of science."[6] Naturally, Huxley attended his funeral, as did twelve other members of the Royal Society.

A funeral Huxley did not attend was that of Sir Richard Owen, who died a scant two months later. But he made it a point to attend a meeting to raise money for a memorial to his old enemy, and in the course of the proceedings he delivered a speech approving a motion for a statue. It was an unusual procedure, Huxley realized, and he justified it in a letter to Foster: "The man did honest work, enough to deserve his statue and that is all that concerns the public."[7] But Huxley's speech was responsible for encouraging Owen's grandson, who was then writing a biography of the scientist, to ask Huxley to contribute a concluding chapter for the book. Huxley complied on the condition that he not be required to make any observations concerning Owen's character. "If I mistake not," Huxley wrote chivalrously, "the historian of comparative anatomy will always assign to Owen a place next to, and hardly lower than that of Cuvier, who was practically the creator of those sciences in their modern shape."[8] But the real value of "Owen's Position in Anatomical Science" is not what it says about Owen but about the growth of the life sciences generally, and it still remains one of the most comprehensive accounts of their progress in nineteenth-century England.

Huxley's health remained good throughout the winter, which he devoted principally to the preparation of the Romanes lecture. "Evolution and Ethics" and the Prologue which he wrote for it afterward are among the most significant writings of his life. "I have been taking an immensity of trouble over it,"[9] he said in April. The difficulties stemmed largely from the stipulations imposed on the address—it must not touch on either religion or politics. A month before the scheduled date of delivery, however, he unexpectedly contracted influenza; and, while his recovery was rapid, it left him with a hoarse voice which made the address inaudible to most of the audience.

Huxley had truly become a living legend in his own time. The announcement of his appearance at Oxford, just a third of a century after the famous meeting of the British Association in 1860, was responsible for a good deal of excitement and anticipation, in America as well as in England; and many of the most famous scientific names of two continents were on hand at the university's Sheldonian Theater to hear the address. Huxley was an impressive figure, by all reports; his gray hair contrasted sharply with his scarlet academic robe; and, except for the inadequacy of his voice, the address was a most satisfactory one.

That summer he made his final trip to Switzerland. On his return he spent most of his time preparing his *Collected Essays* for publication the following year. In these nine volumes most of Huxley's writings on non-scientific subjects are contained. For each volume he wrote a preface; and, though he intended to add a tenth volume with a complete index, the project was never finished. For this reason, some of Huxley's most polished and thoughtful essays, composed during the final three years of his life, are largely unknown to later generations. Among these are "An Apologetic Irenicon," "Professor Tyndall," "Owen's Position in Anatomical Science," and "Mr. Balfour's Attack on Agnosticism."

In his preface to Volume One, partly as an explanation and partly perhaps as an apology, Huxley spoke of his writings as having been "written, for the most part, in the scant leisure of pressing occupations, or in the intervals of ill health ... free neither from superfluities in the way of repetition, nor from deficiencies which ... will be even more conspicuous to other eyes than they are to my own." The excellence of his essays written in the last years, because he had leisure to write as he wished, offers generous evidence that his literary standards grew higher as he got older and that he became one of the most polished of nineteenth-century essayists.

The most shattering personal blow of Huxley's last years was unquestionably the death of John Tyndall in December, 1893. Of all his colleagues, the irrepressible Irish physicist most resembled Huxley in temperament and outlook, although Tyndall lacked Huxley's sense of humor. When Huxley wrote a recollection of Tyndall for the *Nineteenth Century*,[10] he recalled him as an intrepid mountain climber; a dedicated seeker after truth with "a profound distrust of all long chains of deductive reasoning"; a fellow admirer of Carlyle who, however, Huxley adds, "was more disposed to regard Carlyle as a great teacher; I was rather inclined to take him as a great tonic."

And, in respect to the Eyre controversy thirty years before, Huxley writes: "I am afraid that, if things had been pushed to extremities over that unfortunate business, each of us would have been capable of sending the other to the block. But the sentence would have been accompanied by assurances of undiminished respect and devotion." In this very concentrated personal memoir recollection follows upon fond reminiscence with the result that it is, along with being the most affecting piece of writing Huxley ever did, perhaps the only successful writting in a personal vein which he ever did. It stands in strange contrast to his Darwin obituary and his own "Autobiography," which are disconcertingly impersonal and objective.

By 1894 Huxley was already showing apprehension concerning one of the possible outcomes of the rise of science in the twentieth century. In a letter he referred darkly to the "magnitude of evils which accrue from the steady increase of European armaments." For himself he could see no way to check the tendency toward stockpiling weapons and developing others with more sophisticated methods of destruction. "I think that this regrettable fact," he told a man who had requested his signature on a petition urging a treaty limiting armaments, "is merely the superficial expression of social forces, the operation of which cannot be sensibly affected by agreements between governments."[11]

Huxley's health made a visit to Switzerland impossible in 1894, but he was sufficiently recovered by August to make a public appearance at Oxford, where the British Association was holding a meeting for the first time since 1860. The presidential address was delivered by Lord Salisbury, former Prime Minister and a Chancellor of Oxford. When Salisbury rehearsed in his talk the achievements of British science over the course of the nineteenth century, Huxley had the satisfaction of hearing Salisbury refer to the theories of Darwin as being capable of dispute "by no reasonable man." But his ironical reference to the "comforting theory of evolution" reflected the continuing reluctance of many to acknowledge the importance of the most far-reaching advance in biological research achieved to that time.

Lord Kelvin, once one of Darwin's most troublesome critics, moved for a vote of thanks to the speaker. Huxley had been assigned the role of seconding Kelvin's motion, but he had not been entirely happy with the condescension and qualifications contained in Salisbury's talk. In his reply he offered Salisbury a diplomatic rebuke by delivering his own version of the achievements of British science. He did not actually take issue with Salisbury, but discerning listeners noted that his rejoinder dissented completely from the substance of Salisbury's address.

Huxley's participation in the meeting had been a secondary one, but it had the effect of sending him to bed just the same. "I am frightfully tired," he told Hooker a few days later. "But the game was worth the candle."[12]

III *Controversy with Balfour*

In the winter of 1895, Huxley engaged in his last public debate. And, fittingly, it was with a politician—Arthur James Balfour, the Cambridge-educated nephew of Lord Salisbury.[13] An easygoing, detached manner as a young man had led many (including Disraeli) to believe that Balfour lacked character; but he showed great moral courage as a member of Salisbury's cabinet during the 1880's, when, as Chief Secretary for Ireland, he steadfastly opposed all movements favoring Home Rule. On the basis of a book, *A Defense of Philosophic Doubt* (1879), Balfour had acquired for himself something of a reputation as a skeptical philosopher. But it was the publication in 1893 of *The Foundations of Belief,* a book that gained a wide readership, which brought him into controversy with Huxley.

Balfour, after paying appropriate obeisance to science and its methods, had charged Huxley (along with Mill and Spencer) with distorting the findings of science—with, to use his own words, having played "unconscious havoc with the most solid results which empirical methods have hitherto attained."[14] When Huxley was invited by Knowles to reply publicly to the allegation, the request was impossible to refuse.

Huxley, it seems, felt that a well-grounded criticism of science would have had a salutary effect on the climate of English thought; and he approached Balfour's book with a good deal of respect. Part of his esteem for the book was perhaps traceable to Balfour's reputation for possessing one of the keenest minds in Parliament and for being second as a debater only to Bright and Gladstone. As a thinker, of course, he was a long way from antagonists like Gladstone, Argyll, or Principal Wace. Balfour stood opposed to all "systems," and his criticisms of science were not unlike those of Lilly and Mallock.

As has been noted, Lilly had expressed confidence that morality in Huxley would be strong enough to hold its own; but he had then asked: "But will it be strong enough in Professor Huxley's grandchildren?" Lilly feared—and not without reason—that philosophical materialism, supported by the authority of science, was dissolving the moral underpinnings of civilization. Huxley and Lilly were agreed on the essential need for morality; but Lilly felt morality needed the sanction of tradition. Huxley felt that science offered the best hope for finding a basis for moral law.

Balfour had stated his criticism somewhat differently: "Their [Huxley and his followers] spiritual life is parasitic; it is sheltered by convictions which belong not to them, but to the society of which they form a part; it is nourished by processes in which they take no share. And when those convictions decay, and those processes come to an end, the alien life which they have maintained can scarce be expected to outlast them."[15]

Huxley conceded his admiration for Balfour's "charm" of style and his "wit," but his view of Balfour's logic was somewhat different. In a conversation with Wilfred Ward he described the book as being among "the most disappointing he had ever read."[16] Huxley, in fact, felt that Balfour had badly misrepresented the aims and assumptions of science and had described them in extremely vague terms.

Huxley found himself writing at such length in his reply to Balfour that he divided the essay into two parts. "Mr. Balfour's Attack on Agnosticism—Part I" appeared in the *Nineteenth Century* for March, 1895. Huxley quite appropriately described his beginning effort as a "cavalry charge." "I am afraid," he wrote, "that the brilliancy which hovers over the pages of *The Foundations of Belief* is sometimes so vague and shifty that, like a hostile searchlight, it often spreads confusion where it professes to illuminate." Huxley planned to complete his demolition of the book in the second installment and had finished a preliminary draft when he became ill with influenza. From his sickbed he sent a letter to Knowles. "The proofs have just arrived, but I am sorry to say that (I believe for the first time in our transactions) I shall have to disappoint you."[17] The second part of Huxley's reply to Balfour was not destined to see the light in the *Nineteenth Century*. Huxley's condition grew worse, influenza giving way to bronchitis, and subsequent fits of coughing put a severe strain on his heart.

Huxley spent the final four months of his life as an invalid. The inconvenience to which he was putting the other members of the household seems to have been no less a source of discomfort than his malady. "I'm a mere carcass which has to be tended by other people,"[18] he told his son Leonard, when the latter came to Eastbourne on a visit. After a time his condition, already weakened by excessive coughing, was made worse by attacks of nausea. But, even as his condition weakened, he continued to speak gamely of recovery; and the bulk of his conversation concerned the progress of certain plants in his garden.

On June 26th, he sent a letter to Hooker in which he predicted that his "native toughness" would see him through the crisis. Actually, he was in far worse condition than he realized himself; and the shaky hand in which this last letter was written was a truer index to his condition than the optimistic thoughts which it contained. Three days later, on June 29, 1895, Huxley died. At his own request, three lines written by his wife were inscribed on his tomb:

> Be not afraid, ye waiting hearts that weep;
> For still He giveth his beloved sleep,
> And if an endless sleep He wills, so best.

The rough draft of "Mr. Balfour's Attack on Agnosticism—Part II" was not published until 1932, when it was included in Houston Peterson's biography of Huxley. Even in its rough form this article is impressive. Balfour had said that science had denied the existence of reason in the universe. Huxley countered with an argument similar to that advanced in "An Apologetic Irenicon"—citing specifically the example of evolution. "How," he asks, "is evolution conceivable, unless as the development of the energy of the cosmos according to fixed principles towards a definite result?" The universe is governed by a fixed set of rules, and even in such apparently minor matters as the development of a frog the exercise of reason is apparent: "Unless the arrangement of the parts and the disposition of the latent forces of the germ of a frog were rational ... no tadpole would ever emerge from the egg."

On the controversial subject of morality, Balfour had spoken of a moral law which is "immutable, eternal," and which "may be understood even by man, sufficiently for his guidance." Huxley replied by citing the irrelevance of a moral law which could not be understood. If it is beyond man's capacity to divine it, what is its value? And what would be the sense of justice of a God who formulated such a law?

Huxley did good work in demonstrating how imprecise and unscientific Balfour's language was, and how this lack of precision resulted in hazy thinking. But this rejoinder also showed how inflexible Huxley could be. He ignored much of the book that was valuable—for example, Balfour's contention that reason was not the only method of arriving at truth. Huxley's refutation, effective as far as it went, also, characteristically, left many questions unanswered. Still, his superior understanding of the question and his precise, forceful use of language gave him the best of the exchange.

IV *Evolution and Ethics*

Technically, Huxley's reply to Balfour was his last word on the relationship between science and morality; but in "Evolution and Ethics" he actually summarized the drift of his thought during the last decade of his life. After the lecture was delivered, it became almost immediately apparent that most people had misinterpreted Huxley's position as stated in his speech. St. George Mivart, in an article in the August *Nineteenth Century* ("Evolution and Professor Huxley") went so far as to hint that Huxley would soon renounce Darwinism in favor of Catholicism. Another wildly inaccurate interpretation of Huxley's views was advanced by Herbert Spencer, who, in an article in the *Athenaeum*, rather harshly reviewed the address and sharply upbraided Huxley for stealing his ideas.

Spencer's article may not have been altogether a surprise; for, five years before, Huxley's essay "The Struggle for Existence in Human Society" had led to a disagreement between the two men and had highlighted many of their fundamental differences on questions of ethics and morality. Huxley, however, was sensitive to the fact that so many people had failed to understand what he thought he had made plain and clear. But the necessity of skirting religion and politics may have been responsible for some vagueness and consequently for some of the public misapprehension. On more than one occasion Huxley had referred to the lecture as an "egg dance." But he later declared that such widespread misunderstanding may have resulted more from his own mistaken belief that certain propositions which he considered established and which he had "advanced without challenge on former occasions needed no repetition." For this reason he wrote a "Prolegomena,"[19] an explanatory preface in which he restated those ideas. In reply to an observation that the "Prolegomena" was longer than the essay itself, Huxley cited "the precedent of the ancient architects who always made the adytum the smallest part of the temple."

Is ethical nature in essential opposition to cosmic nature? is the question Huxley attempts to answer in the "Prolegomena." Society he describes as an artifice devised by man to serve certain special ends. Man does not adjust to conditions in which he finds himself; instead, he creates new ones under which he can live and prosper. He also establishes codes of law and morality which set limits on the struggle for existence. Social existence— the conditions under which civilized man lives—is analogous in many respects to a garden in which, through the offices of the gardener, the struggle for existence has been eliminated. Instead of natural selection determining those plants which will survive and prosper, these decisions are arrived at through a process of artificial selection. Huxley conceded that ethical nature is part of the cosmic nature; but it is more often than not, in its operations and objectives in opposition to cosmic nature.

In society, he writes, the former struggle—each man against all cosmic nature—is transformed into one of all men against cosmic nature. By eliminating the one for existence within society, man enhances his chances in his struggle against the cosmos. Every stage in the progress of civilization represents a victory of the ethical over the cosmic process and makes man more independent of cosmic nature. Society and ethical nature are products of organic necessity, and their aim is the full development of the capacities of the individual members. However, since the ethical process runs counter to the cosmic process, man must realize that the standards (ethical and moral codes) he in-

vokes to govern society are not absolute nor can they be justified by reference to cosmic nature. As he had suggested, first in
"The Struggle for Existence in Human Society" and later in
"An Apologetic Irenicon," there can be no "ethics of evolution."
Darwinism provides no basis for morality simply because, as has
been noted in the natural world individuals who are the best
ethically are less likely to survive than the worst.

The most characteristic feature of the natural world, Huxley
asserts, is impermanence. If ethical nature represents a victory
of the ethical over the cosmic, that victory is only of temporary duration. Society, like the garden, "is a result of the cosmic process working through and by human energy and intelligence; and as in the case of every other artificial thing set up in
the state of nature, the influences of the latter are constantly
tending to break it down and destroy it." As for the ethical
process itself, Huxley describes it as suppression by individuals
of unrestrained self-assertion in favor of "the organized and per-
sonified sympathy we call conscience." But it does not constitute
complete abandonment of force. In society what in effect occurs
is that men as individuals surrender their rights of unlimited
self-assertion to the state—which acts with the approval of all its
members against individual transgressors of its ethical and moral
codes.

Huxley correctly understood that the evolution of society is
different than that of organisms. The standards by which civilization tends to reward or punish men are widely different from
those operative in the state of nature. But, putting the means
for living into the hands of all men, the struggle has been
eliminated. It had been replaced, Huxley felt, by a struggle
for the means of enjoyment. Huxley concludes the "Prolegomena" with a series of observations concerning society similar to
ideas advanced in "Administrative Nihilism." Positions of leadership and prestige, he says, should go to men of capacity, to
those "endowed with the largest share of energy, of industry, of
intellectual capacity, of tenacity of purpose .... and in so far
as the struggle for the means of enjoyment tends to place such
men in possession of wealth and influence, it is a process which
tends to the good of society."

Toward the close of the century, not a few scientists who had supported Darwin began to shy away from his beliefs. Lyell and Wallace are examples of scientists who had originally been close to Darwin but who eventually had second thoughts about the consequences of evolutionary speculation and who ended their days as adherents of some form or other of religious belief. To this list can also be added the name of G. J. Romanes, a former student of Darwin, who as early as 1876 (in *A Candid Examination of Theism*) declared himself to be critical of the sudden rise of science and described the advance of science as "a deluge, black with destruction, restless in might, uprooting our most cherished hopes, engulfing our most precious creed, and burying our highest life in mindless desolation."[20]

Huxley, needless to say, shared none of the apprehension of Romanes, and would have liked nothing better than to use his Romanes lecture as an opportunity to chart the impact of science upon religion and politics. In 1899 Huxley had spoken of religion and politics as being the two subjects "that ought to interest a man more than any others,"[21] and they were in fact seldom far from his own mind in the decade after his retirement from the School of Mines in 1885. He was not altogether dismayed by Romanes's prohibition against any mention of the subjects in the lecture, however; and he attempted to sidestep the prohibition by concentrating his attention on the religious doctrines of Greece, India, and the Orient. "If people apply anything I say to modern philosophies ... and religions," he told Romanes, "that is not my affair. To be honest, however, unless I thought they would, I should never have taken all the pains I have bestowed on these thirty-six pages."[22]

The views advanced in the "Prolegomena" were generally harsh and fatalistic, but those of "Evolution and Ethics"[23] are, if anything, harsher yet. Both essays represent an attempt to employ Darwinism as the basis for philosophical and moral speculation; but, because Huxley felt the cosmic process to be antagonistic to morality and ethics, his conclusions are largely quite bleak. He begins by rejecting "modern pessimism" because there is a slight chance, he feels, that ethical nature may continue to triumph over cosmic nature. Moreover, the history of mankind offers hope that man may yet continue to make progress in this respect: "Fragile reed as he may be, man, as

Pascal says, is a thinking reed: there lies within him a fund of
energy operating intelligently and ... competent to influence
and modify the cosmic process." These are among the few
hopeful sentiments in the essay.

Huxley, of course, was not the first to advance such a view of
life. Darwin himself had perceived the pessimistic conclusions
to which the theory of organic evolution led and, as an antidote,
had counseled that there was "nobility" in this (the evolutionary) view. Arthur Schopenhauer and John Stuart Mill had attempted, before Huxley, to apply the new biological discoveries
to the ethical realm; but their conclusions reflect little of the
nobility of which Darwin spoke. Nor is there much optimism
in the conclusions reached by Huxley since all is based on
chance that man may use his abilities.

In the "Prolegomena" Huxley analyzed the origins of society;
in "Evolution and Ethics" he concentrated his attention on society itself. Man, according to Huxley, "has worked his way to
the headship of the sentient world ... in virtue of his success in
struggle for existence." Civilization, as men know it, is unquestionably one of the most remarkable products of the cosmic
process; but civilized man finds himself entangled in a strange
paradox. Having mitigated the struggle for existence, man
finds himself with a new burden—thought. He now wants to
"make existence intelligible and to bring the order of things into
harmony" with his moral sense. Clearly he owes his dominant
position on the planet to the "ape and tiger" within him; but to
continue to give unlimited self-assertion to these tendencies is to
act in defiance of the ethical and moral codes which are the basis
of his social existence.

As has already been noted, man has from the earliest times attempted to explain injustice and the capriciousness of fate by
appealing to religion. In his survey of ancient religious doctrines, Huxley finds that the Greek, the Semite, and the Indian
are agreed that there is "unfathomable injustice in the nature of
things." But each of them failed, despite their attempts, to reconcile the moral indifference in nature to the ethical conduct
of man. Buddhism attempted to account for the inequities of
existence by the doctrine of transmigration, which postulates
that individuals reap in later existences according to what they

have sown in antecedent existences. The resemblance of this explanation to Christian belief is obvious, but Huxley questions "whether the cosmic process looks any more moral ... after such a vindication."

Indian philosophy, on the other hand, is more appealing to Huxley since it excludes any reference to the supernatural. Indian sages recommend withdrawal from life to take up the mantle of the anchorite. What all these philosophies have in common is their being pervaded by views similar to those of modern science (specifically, evolutionary)—that life is a succession of cycles and that change is a constant factor in human existence.

The failing of the most substantial philosophy to come out of Greece—the Stoic—is that it did not recognize that cosmic nature is antagonistic to ethical nature. The Stoics erred by thinking they could find support for their doctrines in cosmic nature, in their insistence on regarding "the cosmos as a pedagogue to virtue." It is rather strange to see Huxley, who in his earliest writings frequently proclaimed his unswerving faith in the Stoic view of life, recanting this belief. Altogether, Huxley feels that Greek, Indian, and Oriental thought converge toward a similar end: "By the Tiber, as by the Ganges, ethical man admits that the cosmos is too strong for him; and, destroying every bond which ties him to it by ascetic discipline, he seeks salvation in absolute renunciation."

V *Conclusion*

The Victorian era is generally considered to have produced the bulk of the greatest English prose literature, and in this respect it enjoys a place analogous to that of the Elizabethan in drama. And few would object to a grouping which would include Huxley among the seven or eight leading essayists of the age. At the same time, Huxley would be perhaps the only one of these writers who for the better part of his life was not self-consciously a man of letters. The greater part of his time was devoted to public affairs and to original research; but, as he grew older, he became more and more serious about his literary activity. He attested to rewriting his essays as many as half a dozen times; and, when he undertook to collect his non-scientific writings in 1892, it was plainly with an awareness that people would be reading them after his death. He was not unaware, therefore, of the quality of permanence in these essays and of their claim on the attention of posterity.

Indeed, toward the end of his life he was not above commenting on the standards which he attempted to meet in his writing. On one occasion he spoke of the importance of using language "with precision, with force, and with art."[24] As far as his own writing went, he sometimes used language with too much "force," and the result was a habit of handing down opinions *ex cathedra* which is at times more than a little annoying. However, one is not as a rule likely to be offended by the forthrightness of Huxley since his dogmatism seems to have its source in sincere enthusiasm rather than in a desire to force the reader into reluctant assent.

"I venture to doubt," he once declared, "the wisdom of attempting to mould one's style by any other process than that of striving after the clear and forcible expression of definite conceptions; in which process the ... precept, 'first catch your definite conceptions,' is probably the most difficult to obey."[25] But the picture one has of Huxley—that of a writer who is more than anything else a master of plain, unadorned English—is not an entirely accurate one. Huxley's earlier essays, by and large, exhibit these characteristics; but, as time passed, he became more and more inclined to swathe relatively uncomplicated ideas in heavily rhetorical and even ornate language. Moreover, he often digressed to make relatively minor points, relied heavily on metaphors, and his references and allusions are frequently quite eclectic. His language is rakish, sprinkled with biblical constructions, and influenced by those writers he most admired—chiefly Hobbes, Addison, and Locke. Perhaps the critic who best summed up Huxley's achievement as a man of letters was H. L. Mencken, who called Huxley "the greatest of all masters of orderly exposition. He taught me the importance of giving to every argument a simple structure."[26]

The productions of no writer are immune to the inroads of time, least of all writers who address themselves to subjects of more or less transient interest, to social reform, or to controversy. To a certain extent, Huxley's work has dated; but a solid body of sound literature remains which bears the imprint of a great craftsman and which may yet spark a Huxley revival in the twentieth century.

In such essays as "Animal Automatism," "Descartes," "The Physical Basis of Life," and certain chapters in the Hume book, Huxley, in charting the impact of scientific thought on philosophy, came to grips with problems that remain pertinent and significant. Some of the answers given by Huxley to these problems are too simple to entirely satisfy the twentieth-century reader, and his habit of applying mechanical principles to account for the operation of man's mind seems today to smack too heavily of what has come to be known as "reductionism"; he frequently failed to take into account aspects of a problem which were more involved than he seems to have realized. But the questions which he set out to answer in these essays—and in some cases he gave answers that have not been bettered since—have not altered much in the intervening years.

So far as theology goes, Huxley's writings do not have, nor had they ever, so wide an appeal. "Hasiadra's Adventure," in which he ingeniously questioned the veracity of the biblical account of the flood and therefore of the entire Old Testament, and "Witness to the Miraculous," in which he showed how the post- and prescientific approach to natural phenomena differ from each other, probably remain to this day as good as anything ever written on these subjects. But the controversial essays have not held up nearly so well with the passage of time.

In recording the impact of evolutionary thought upon ethics and morality—"The Struggle for Existence in Human Society," "An Apologetic Irenicon," and "Evolution and Ethics"—he was among the first to thoroughly explore a question about which a whole library has since grown. Moreover, the conclusions reached by Huxley in these essays are quite valid today; in fact, they remain the basis for much of the thought on these questions.

Chiefly of biographical interest are "The Reception of the Origin of Species" (written for the Darwin biography), *The Rattlesnake Journal*, "Prologue to *Controverted Questions*," "Autobiography," and "Professor Tyndall." These essays, which shed light on some aspect or other of Huxley's character, should be read by anyone with an interest in Huxley or his times. Although his essays on behalf of Darwin are primarily of historical interest today, *Man's Place in Nature* has obtained a permanent place in the history of English science, as well as of English letters. The questions Huxley set out to answer in this epoch-making volume are not entirely "inclosed in the rubble of the foundations of later knowledge," as Huxley modestly declared in his preface to the 1893 volume of the book. "On a Piece of Chalk" has of course become an acknowledged classic of scientific exposition. Probably of least interest to the twentieth-century reader are his essays on educational reform, in which he gave expressions to ideas which have become so much a part of the modern view of education that there is hardly any reason to reread them.

From Carlyle, Huxley imbibed a deep dislike for sham and pretense; his lifelong warfare against "humbugs," whether religious (Wilberforce), political (Gladstone), or scientific (Owen), is one of the more striking aspects of his career. Huxley greatly enjoyed smiting the old orthodoxy in the name of the new; but his favorite opponents in this regard were, by all odds, clerics. One of Huxley's more ingenious arguments in his long campaign against ecclesiastical authority rested on his claim that men of science were actually more "moral" than men of the cloth. This assertion was so, Huxley said, because scientists did not affirm as truths anything that had not been subjected to clear and indisputable proof by experiment and verification. This is a clever argument and certainly has much to be said for it, but the fact remains that Huxley never really defined the standard of reliable evidence. Huxley was here hitting revealed religion at its weakest point; but he also was forgetting that the postulates of science are in many respects no different from those of many other varieties of knowledge. Huxley knew this well enough, and it is to be recalled that he defined science on more than one occasion "as nothing but trained and organized common sense."

Because of his enormous success as a debunker and iconoclast the picture of Huxley that has come down to us is one of a swashbuckling defender of truth who effectively proved that industry, honesty, and intelligence were mightier weapons than deviousness, bluff, and insularity. Huxley, however, was disconcertingly aware of the part he had played in the intellectual history of England in the nineteenth century. In a letter written in 1891, for example, he told a friend that his "sole motive is to get

[*159*]

at the truth in all things." Huxley frequently made grandiose claims on his own behalf in his later years; and, while many naïve commentators have solemnly taken them at face value, more sophisticated observers have had a good deal of fun at Huxley's expense because of these less than modest assertions.

In *The New Republic* William Mallock has Mr. Storks (Huxley) humorlessly announce to the assembly that there must be a "universal, intrepid, dogged resolve to find out and face the complete truth of things, and to allow no prejudice, however dear to us, to obscure our vision."[27] William James, too, declared himself unable to subscribe to "what seems to be becoming the conventionally accepted view of Huxley, that he possessed the exclusive specialty of living for the truth. A good deal of humbug about that!—at least when it becomes a professional heroic attitude."[28]

Huxley died five years before the turn of the century, but through his work as a scientist and as an educator he exercised an influence that continues to this day. Huxley, indeed, was so much the spokesman for what has become the accepted view in many areas of thought, that one tends to forget that there ever was any opposition to Darwinism or to the introduction of science into school and university curriculums. But his influence continues in another, much larger, sense—in his habits of thought and in his recognition of certain important basic ideas. If the day is forever past (and let us hope it is) when "aesthetic" meant, as Thomas Beer remarked in *The Mauve Decade,* an essay by Walter Pater, it is at least in part due to Huxley's continuing insistence that the sciences and the humanities were not susceptible to the separate compartmentalization people were attempting to impose upon them.

It is perhaps as a champion of Darwin that he is chiefly remembered now, but it is less generally known that Huxley was among the first to appreciate the far-reaching implications of Darwinian theory in other areas of thought. Today theologians, philosophers, sociologists, and men of letters—no less than scientists—acknowledge their debt to Darwin; but few nineteenth-century thinkers besides Huxley appreciated the impact that man's new knowledge of his origins would have on other areas of thought—areas that previously had been considered to be exclusively within the province of letters. Although Huxley had little sympathy for Bacon ("I have been oppressed by the humbug of 'Baconian Induction' all my life," he declared in 1881), he resembled Bacon in his belief in a universal system of knowledge similar to the *Prima Philosophia* described (however vaguely and inadequately) by Bacon.

By the close of the nineteenth century, the sciences comprised a fund of knowledge capable of telling a student a great deal about the nature of the world and of men; and they merited the same close, careful study that until that time had been given largely to humanistic subjects. Many Victorians, however, continued to believe that an exclusively humanistic education would suffice to produce a completely educated man. Even such eminent contemporaries of Huxley as Carlyle and Arnold, both of whom were familiar with the general drift of science and its basic premises, believed this concept to be true and failed to recognize the new prestige science had won. Certainly one of Huxley's greatest accomplishments was the acquisition of a new respect for science and scientists. According to William Irvine, it is "part of Huxley's importance that ... he brought the man of science as a cultural type into the broader area of European civilization."[29] The great evolution controversy had offered Huxley his chance; and seizing it, he played a large role in permanently altering the basic thought patterns of the educated Europeans.

Huxley's last essays demonstrate how deeply pessimistic he had become. As a young man, his firmly held belief in the ability of science to solve many of the problems of men had tended to counterbalance the fatalism that had always underlain his thought. But Huxley's confident optimism began to vanish as he grew older; science clearly was not serving men in the noble manner for which he had hoped. Scientific discoveries have frequently eroded man's confidence in older doctrines; but, by and large, they have failed to provide a basis for "the new morality" which Huxley envisioned. The arrival of the twentieth century found man, so to speak, in an intellectual cul-de-sac. And even at this moment the way out is not yet clear. The principal function of scientific research in the years since Huxley's death has been to function as a basis for technology, a development that has provided man with increased comforts and leisure but not with a system of ideals or answers to the riddles of existence. Huxley had prophetically voiced concern that science would be employed exclusively in such a fashion as early as 1866 when, in his essay "On the Adviseableness of Improving Natural Knowledge," he declared that men are inclined to regard natural knowledge as nothing more than "a fairy godmother, ready to furnish her pets with shoes of swiftness, swords of sharpness, and omnipotent Aladdin's lamps, so that they may have telegraphs to Saturn and see the other side of the moon." Huxley, of course, was quite anxious to disassociate himself from such a view. "If this talk were true," he continues, "I would just as soon be quietly chipping my own flint axe after the manner of my forefathers a few thousand years back."

In the last analysis, Huxley can be said to have helped provide science with its initial momentum, but it must be conceded that he was unable to control the direction which it proceeded to take. Science has not been the liberating force which Huxley hoped it would be—at least not for the bulk of mankind. Perhaps he claimed too much for the discipline; perhaps it is still too early to tell.

Notes and References

Preface

1. *Nature*, LII (1895), p. 528.
2. Aldous Huxley, *The Olive Tree* (London, 1936), p. 50.

Chapter One

1. *Methods and Results*, p. 7.
2. "Science at Sea: Narrative of the Voyage of the *H.M.S. Rattlesnake*," *Westminster Review*, LXI (1854), p. 100.
3. *Ibid.*, p. 100.
4. Leonard Huxley, *Life and Letters of Thomas Henry Huxley* (New York, 1901), I, 40.
5. Beatrice Webb, *My Apprenticeship* (New York and London, 1926), p. 28.
6. *Methods and Results*, p. 13.
7. *Life and Letters*, I, 75.
8. *Ibid.*, p. 140.
9. *Ibid.*, p. 138.
10. *Ibid.*, p. 154.
11. Leonard Huxley, father of Julian and Aldous Huxley, married a niece of Matthew Arnold in 1885. Besides collecting the letters of his father, he also compiled the correspondence of Sir Joseph Hooker.
12. *Life and Letters*, I, 162.
13. His position as naturalist to the Geological Survey awakened Huxley's interest in paleontology. His first scientific paper on paleontology was written in 1856 and by 1871 his paleontological papers numbered thirty-eight.
14. *Scientific Memoirs*, I, 129.
15. *Science and Education*, pp. 38–66.
16. William Irvine, *Apes, Angels, and Victorians* (New York, 1955), p. 37.
17. Francis Darwin, ed., *The Life and Letters of Charles Darwin* (New York, 1959), I, 549–50.
18. Herbert Spencer, *Essays Scientific, Political, Speculative* (New York, 1892), p. 6.

19. Charles Lyell (1797–1875) wrote *Principles of Geology*, which caused British geologists to re-estimate their assumptions as to the antiquity of the earth. Lyell, who enormously influenced Darwin, introduced the idea of uniformitarianism—that geological phenomena are the result of generally constant natural forces operating over great spans of time.

20. Benjamin Disraeli, *Tancred* (London, 1847), I, 225.

21. *British and Foreign Medical Review*, XIII (1854), pp. 332–43.

22. *Scientific Memoirs*, I, 305–14.

23. *Ibid.*, p. 311.

24. *Ibid.*, pp. 538–606.

25. *Life and Letters*, I, 101.

26. *Ibid.*, p. 172.

Chapter Two

1. The theory that organisms evolve by a process of natural selection was contained in a paper co-authored by Darwin and Alfred Russell Wallace read before the Linnaen Society on July 1, 1858. Wallace had independently arrived at conclusions similar to Darwin's and had communicated his findings to Darwin while the latter was writing the *Origin*.

2. *Life and Letters*, I, 189.

3. *Darwiniana*, pp. 1–21.

4. *Life and Letters*, I, 224.

5. *Darwiniana*, pp. 22–80.

6. *Ibid.*, pp. 22–23.

7. Huxley advanced evidence to counter Owen's claim in an article written for the *Natural History Review*, I (1861), pp. 67–84. Huxley had, in fact, been instrumental in founding the periodical. It lasted only four years; however, Huxley also aided Leslie Konyer in establishing *Nature* (1869). For the first number Huxley contributed an English translation of Goethe's essay in praise of nature.

8. Wilberforce had been coached for this talk by Owen. He had, moreover, contributed an anonymous article to the *Quarterly Review* in which, after describing the *Origin* as a "most readable book," he went on to demonstrate why the hypothesis was unsupported by the facts. Huxley later described the article as an "outpouring of preposterous incapacity."

9. Wilberforce's opinion of Darwin's claim for scientific eminence was probably similar to Owen's. Owen had reviewed the *Origin* (for the *Edinburgh Review*) and had predicted that it would be forgotten within ten years.

10. This quotation is contained in a letter written by John Richard Green, an undergraduate who was in the audience, to a friend. Leonard Huxley calls it "the fullest and probably most accurate" account of his father's words. He qualifies the statement, however, with the recollection that his father once mentioned not having used the word "equivocal" in his reply. No verbatim reports of what was said exist. Leonard Huxley has assembled the published recollections of all who were present (*Life and Letters*, Vol. I, Chap. 14), and most are in general agreement, though they differ in detail. Francis Darwin also included an account of the meeting in *The Life and Letters of Charles Darwin*.

11. Jacques Barzun, *Darwin, Marx, and Wagner* (New York, 1958), p. 64.

12. *Darwiniana*, pp. 303–475.

13. *Ibid.*, p. 373.

14. *Life and Letters*, I, 223.

15. *Man's Place in Nature and Other Essays*, pp. 1–208. Three other essays on ethnology, rather speculative and somewhat dated in their assumptions, are also included in this volume—"On the Methods and Results of Ethnology" (1865); "On Some Fixed Points in British Ethnology" (1871); "On the Aryan Question" (1890). The preface Huxley wrote for this volume is of great historical interest.

16. Darwin confidently altered the sentence to read "Much light . . ." for the sixth edition.

17. *Man's Place*, pp. x–xi.

18. *Life and Letters*, II, 365.

19. *Life and Letters*, I, 217.

20. "Huxley as Anthropologist," Supplement to *Nature*, May 9, 1925, p. 722.

21. *Man's Place*, pp. 154–55.

22. Mrs. Charles Kingsley, ed., *Charles Kingsley: Letters and Memories of His Life* (London, 1899), p. 253.

23. *Darwiniana*, p. 229. This address, "On the Coming of the Age of the 'Origin of Species,'" is at once compact and illuminating. The progress of science, Huxley says, is the history of a continuing warfare of truth against ignorance. Evolution won quick acceptance because of the fortunate confluence of a variety of sciences. Darwin's hypothesis was substantiated by the researches of geologists and paleontologists as well as biologists and embryologists.

24. *Ibid.*, pp. 80–106.

25. *Ibid.*, pp. 120–86.

26. *Ibid.*, p. 111.

27. *Ibid.*, p. 148.

28. *Discourses Biological and Geological*, p. 333.

Chapter Three

1. *Life and Letters*, I, 106. Huxley's earliest platform efforts were not very successful. The art was one he worked very hard to cultivate.

2. *Ibid.*, p. 149.

3. "A Lobster; or, the Study of Zoology," *Discourses Biological and Geological*, pp. 196–229.

4. *Discourses Biological and Geological*, pp. 1–36.

5. Quoted by Cyril Bibby, *Huxley, Scientist, Humanist and Educator*, p. 98.

6. *Discourses Biological and Geological*, p. 5.

7. *Ibid.*, pp. 137–61.

8. *Ibid.*, p. 159.

9. *Methods and Results*, pp. 18–42.

10. *Ibid.*, pp. 130–65.

11. *Science and Education*, p. 151.

12. *Methods and Results*, p. 31.

13. Huxley's views on the question were concisely stated in a letter written to Charles Kingsley five years before: "My fundamental axiom of speculative philosophy is that *materialism and spiritualism are opposite poles of the same absurdity*—the absurdity of imagining that we know anything about either spirit or matter."

14. *Methods and Results*, p. 161.

15. *Discourses Biological and Geological*, pp. vii–viii.

Chapter Four

1. Lytton Strachey, *Eminent Victorians* (New York, 1918), p. 201.

2. These essays are all contained in *Science and Education*.

3. *Ibid.*, p. 86.

4. W. H. Mallock, *Memoirs of Life and Literature* (London, 1920), p. 63.

5. In 1870 Huxley was appointed to two Royal Commissions. At the time he was also president of the Ethnological Society. The following year he was appointed secretary of the Royal Society. In 1872 he became president of the Geological Society.

6. *Science and Education*, pp. 374–403.

7. James Knowles (1831–1908), at this time editor of the *Contemporary Review*, later founded the *Nineteenth Century*, which under his guidance became one of the most influential of English periodicals. An architect by training, Knowles was personally acquainted with just about every Victorian of eminence. He was co-founder, with Tennyson, of the Metaphysical Society.

8. *Science and Education,* p. 122. The contemporary who was closest to Huxley's views on the place of science in education was F. W. Farrar, a master at Harrow. Huxley's campaign was strongly aided by Farrar's support. See "Public School Education," *Fortnightly,* IV (March, 1868).

9. *Ibid.,* pp. 179–80.

10. Poor instruction in science, Huxley felt, was actually worse than none at all. In his address at Aberdeen he spoke of himself as "strongly inclined to agree with the learned school-masters who say that, in their experience, the teaching of science is a waste of time. As they teach it," he declared, "I have no doubt it is."

11. *Science and Education,* pp. 203–04.

12. *Ibid.,* p. 423.

13. *Science and Education,* p. 434.

14. These essays are contained in *Science and Education.*

15. *Life and Letters,* I, 392.

16. *Ibid.,* pp. 449–50.

17. *Ibid.,* p. 450.

18. *Ibid.,* p. 493.

19. *Ibid.,* p. 494.

20. *Ibid.,* p. 495.

21. *Ibid.,* p. 496.

22. *Science and Hebrew Tradition,* pp. 46, 139.

23. *Ibid.,* p. 115.

24. *Life and Letters,* I, 502.

25. Matthew Arnold, *Discourses in America* (London, 1885), p. 94.

26. *Ibid.,* p. 129.

Chapter Five

1. The argument of this paper served as the basis for Chapter IX of Huxley's volume on Hume.

2. James Hinton, *The Lawbreaker* (London, 1884), p. 154.

3. *Hume, With Helps to the Study of Berkeley,* p. 43.

4. *Life and Letters,* I, 258. Huxley sent Kingsley three long letters during 1863, in addition to the letter sent after the death of his son.

5. *Ibid.,* p. 233.

6. *Ibid.,* p. 235.

7. *Methods and Results,* pp. 192–93.

8. *Ibid.,* pp. 199–250. This essay was delivered as an address to the 1874 meeting of the British Association at Belfast. Three days before, Tyndall had given the inaugural address in which he described physical science as "impregnable" and eternally antagonistic to all forms of re-

ligion. The reaction had been so stormy Huxley had momentarily considered altering his own address for fear of further criticism. At the last moment, though, he delivered the address as originally planned. "I must grasp the nettle," he is reported to have remarked at the time.
9. *Ibid.*, p. 244.
10. Another thinker, who along with Descartes and Hume, Huxley recognized as a spiritual kin was Joseph Priestley; and, when in 1874 he delivered an address on Priestley on the occasion of the erection of a statue in his honor, Huxley used the occasion to comment on Priestley's philosophy. Priestley was close to Huxley in his doctrines of materialism and necessity and, like Huxley, did not believe in free will, the existence of a soul, or the immortality of man. Priestley, however, reconciled science with Scripture by declaring that man would be raised from the dead by "a direct exertion of the power of God" and would from that time on be immortal. Huxley, of course, did not subscribe to this particular concession by Priestley to orthodoxy any more than he did to Descartes' belief in man's soul.
11. Huxley's first contact with philosophical skepticism came from reading Goethe. Huxley adopted Goethe's concept of *tätige skepsis*—the active skepticism which has as an objective its own self-destruction—as an intellectual ideal while still in his twenties. From that time on he made it a point never to rest this thought on any arbitrary authority. He also had a firsthand acquaintance with other German philosophers—Kant, Hegel, Lessing, Novalis, and Schopenhauer. But his respect for Germans as thinkers was limited. "As men of research in positive science," he once said, "they are magnificently laborious and accurate. But most of them have no notion of style and they seem to compose their books with a pitchfork."
12. *Hume, With Helps to the Study of Berkeley,* p. 189.
13. *Ibid.,* pp. 243–319.

Chapter Six

1. *Life and Letters,* II, 57–58.
2. Michael Foster (1836–1907), Pra-elector in Physiology, Trinity College, Cambridge, and co-author with Huxley of *Elementary Physiology.* In later years, he was one of Huxley's closest confidants.
3. *Life and Letters,* II, 77.
4. *Ibid.,* II, 105.
5. *Ibid.,* II, 111.
6. *Life and Letters,* II, 350.
7. *Methods and Results,* p. 156.

8. Congreve, who studied with Dr. Arnold at Rugby and was later a fellow of Wadham College, Oxford, met Comte twice, once in Paris after the Revolution of 1848 and again in 1857.

9. T. H. Huxley, "The Scientific Aspects of Positivism," *Fortnightly Review*, V (February, 1869).

10. Morley, for example, seemed to become surfeited with Comte rather suddenly. His article on Positivism for the *Encyclopaedia Britannica* (1876) reflects a good deal of disenchantment with humanity worship; a development probably directly attributable to Huxley.

11. "Gladstone, Samuel of Oxford, and Owen," Huxley said in 1892, "belong to a very curious type of humanity, with many excellent and even great qualities and one fatal defect—utter untrustworthiness."

12. F. W. Hirst, *Early Life and Letters of John Morley* (London, 1927 II, 46.

13. *Life and Letters*, I, 341.

14. *Science and Christian Tradition*, p. 252.

15. *Life and Letters*, II, 124. The effect of Gladstone's apologetics, Huxley later said, was to send him "blaspheming about the house with the first healthy expression of wrath" he had exhibited in several years.

16. *Science and Hebrew Tradition*, pp. 139–63.

17. *Ibid.*, pp. 160–61.

18. *Life and Letters*, II, 123.

19. *Nineteenth Century*, XIX (January, 1886), pp. 1–12.

20. *Science and Hebrew Tradition*, p. 168.

21. *Life and Letters*, II, 144. Although he opposed independence and heartily disliked Gladstone, Huxley had a genuine admiration of Parnell. The sudden fall of the Irish leader left him with mixed feelings. "I wonder if the G. O. M. ever swears?" Huxley asked in 1890. "Pity if he can't have that relief just now."

22. *Life and Letters*, II, 139.

23. *Evolution and Ethics and Other Essays*, p. 118.

24. *Science and Christian Tradition*, p. 78.

25. *Ibid.*, p. 123.

26. Like so many of Huxley's other antagonists, Argyll was a prominent political figure, having served in numerous liberal cabinets. He was, moreover, a close friend of Gladstone and of Sir Richard Owen. Gladstone and Argyll held opposing views on the question of Home Rule but remained, nevertheless, on the best terms, probably because they shared many common beliefs and aims. Both felt it to be of the greatest importance to reconcile the new discoveries of science with the revealed truths of Christianity. Like Huxley, Argyll had been precocious in science and was voted a member of the Royal Society at twenty-eight. A lifelong opponent of the views of Darwin, he served for a time

as the president of the British Association and was clearly trading on his reputation as a scientist in his controversy with Huxley.

27. *Ibid.*, p. 134.

28. *Life and Letters*, II, 193.

29. *Science and Christian Tradition*, pp. 209–62.

30. *Nineteenth Century*, XXV (March, 1889), pp. 351–71. Magee also replied in this issue. He said that he had not intended to imply that all agnostics were "cowardly." He described the creed as "a pleasant shelter from the trouble of thought and the pain and effort of self-denial."

31. *Science and Christian Tradition*, pp. 263–308.

32. *Life and Letters*, II, 240. According to Cyril Bibby, Huxley had an advantage of which his opponents were unaware: the editor was on his side. When it was not possible to provide proofs of articles by Gladstone and Argyll, Knowles sent advance copies at the first possible moment; and, when Huxley wanted to be sure of having the last word in his argument with Wace, the editor was very ready to agree. See "Huxley: Prince of Controversialists" (*Twentieth Century*, March, 1957), p. 275.

33. In a letter to Tyndall in 1891, the Duke of Argyll expressed the wish that Huxley "would not write so offensively. I can understand the agnostic frame of mind perfectly, but I can't understand making it so aggressive. He writes as if every believer in Christianity were no better than the black beetle beneath his feet" (*Autobiography and Memoirs* [London, 1906], II, 526).

34. Huxley himself may have been aware of their inadequacies, for he elaborated on the theme of these essays in "The Lights of the Church and the Lights of Science" (*Nineteenth Century*, July, 1890). He again states that Christian theology is necessarily dependent on the historical accuracy of the entire Old Testament. If the story of the flood, for example, is not literally true, then the entire Bible comes into question.

35. *Huxley: Prophet of Science*, p. 247.

36. Paul Elmer More, *The Drift of Romanticism* (Boston, 1913), p. 211.

37. *Science and Christian Tradition*, pp. 1–2.

Chapter Seven

1. *Life and Letters*, II, 203.

2. *Ibid.*, p. 225.

3. *Methods and Results*, pp. 290–336.

4. *Life and Letters*, II, 261.

5. *Methods and Results*, p. 358.

6. *Evolution and Ethics and Other Essays,* pp. 46–117.

7. *Methods and Results,* pp. 383–430.

8. *Ibid.,* pp. 251–90.

9. Quoted by Cyril Bibby in *Huxley,* p. 31.

10. *Life and Letters,* I, 302.

11. *Ibid.,* p. 305.

12. See "Conclusion," *The Impregnable Rock of Holy Scripture* (Philadelphia, 1896).

13. *Science and Christian Tradition,* pp. 366–92.

14. *Ibid.,* pp. 393–419.

15. *Life and Letters,* II, 421.

16. *Evolution and Ethics and Other Essays,* p. 238. Huxley reprinted these letters in this volume under the heading "Social Diseases and Worse Remedies."

17. *Life and Letters,* II, 289.

18. *Science and Christian Tradition,* p. 21.

19. *Ibid.,* pp. 21–22.

20. *Ibid.,* pp. 93–94.

21. In "Hasiadra's Adventure," one of his more ingenious essays, Huxley by calling the likelihood of the story of Hasiadra (an ancient Semitic tale similar to the story of the flood) into question, also casts doubt on the Hebrew account. Although the story of Hasiadra itself contains no details beyond the bounds of possibility, it stands beyond the bounds of probability since the account of the tale is contained on one of a series of twelve cuneiform tablets on which are also contained stories of Bel, Istar, Idzubar, and other Chaldean deities. These stories, according to Huxley, all stand or fall together. And, since the story of Hasiadra can hardly be regarded as a historical verity, neither can the Hebrew account of the deluge which is based upon it.

22. *Science and Hebrew Tradition,* pp. 287–372.

23. *Life and Letters,* II, 240.

24. *Life and Letters,* I, 237.

25. *Life and Letters,* II, 361.

Chapter Eight

1. *Life and Letters,* II, 317.

2. *Science and Christian Tradition,* p. 256.

3. *Evolution and Ethics and Other Essays,* p. 200.

4. *Life and Letters,* II, 345.

5. *Ibid.,* p. 349.

6. *Ibid.,* p. 359.

7. *Ibid.,* p. 361.

8. Richard Startin Owen, *The Life of Richard Owen* (London, 1894–95), II, 312.

9. *Life and Letters*, II, 374.

10. "Professor Tyndall," *Nineteenth Century*, XXXV (January, 1894).

11. *Life and Letters*, II, 397.

12. *Ibid.*, p. 401.

13. Balfour's younger brother Francis Maitland Balfour (1851–82) was a protégé of Huxley's. Huxley regarded him highly, and his untimely death from a fall in the Alps was a heavy loss for English science.

14. A. J. Balfour, *The Foundations of Belief* (New York and London, 1895), p. 124.

15. *Ibid.*, p. 83.

16. *Life and Letters*, II, 420.

17. *Ibid.*, p. 423.

18. *Ibid.*, p. 425.

19. *Evolution and Ethics*, pp. 1–45.

20. George Romanes, *A Candid Examination of Theism* (London, 1878), p. 52.

21. *Life and Letters*, II, 237.

22. *Ibid.*, p. 375.

23. *Evolution and Ethics*, pp. 46–116.

24. *Science and Education*, p. 185.

25. *Life and Letters*, II, 302.

26. "Mencken Remembered," *American Scholar*, XXXII (1963), p. 270.

27. William Mallock, *The New Republic* (London, 1877), p. 56.

28. Henry James, ed., *Life and Letters of William James* (Boston, 1920), II, 348.

29. *Apes, Angels, and Victorians*, p. 117.

Selected Bibliography

PRIMARY SOURCES

1. Books

In this selective bibliography no attempt has been made to list scientific works that would not interest the general reader. A comprehensive but not complete list of Huxley's publications—literary and scientific—is contained in Leonard Huxley's indispensable *Life and Letters of Thomas Henry Huxley.* A select list of Huxley's publications is given by Cyril Bibby in *T. H. Huxley, Scientist, Humanist, and Educator.* Huxley collected his miscellaneous articles, essays, and lectures in his *Collected Essays,* most of which he reprinted unaltered. His scientific works, collected by E. Ray Lankester and Michael Foster, were published posthumously.

Evidence as to Man's Place in Nature. London: Williams and Norgate, 1863.

Lessons in Elementary Physiology. London: Macmillan and Co., 1866.

Lay Sermons, Addresses, and Reviews. London: Macmillan and Co., 1870.

Critiques and Addresses. London: Macmillan and Co., 1873.

A Course of Practical Instruction in Elementary Biology (with H. N. Martin). London: Macmillan and Co., 1875.

American Addresses. London: Macmillan and Co., 1877.

Physiography. London: Macmillan and Co., 1877.

Hume (English Men of Letters Series). London: Macmillan and Co., 1878.

Science and Culture and Other Essays. London: Macmillan and Co., 1881.

Social Diseases and Worse Remedies. London: Macmillan and Co., 1891.

Essays on Some Controverted Questions. London: Macmillan and Co., 1892.

Evolution and Ethics (The Romanes Lecture, 1893). London: Macmillan and Co., 1893.

Collected Essays. 9 vols. London: Macmillan and Co., 1893–94. (I. *Methods and Results;* II. *Darwiniana;* III. *Science and Education;* IV. *Science and Hebrew Tradition;* V. *Science and Christian Tra-*

dition; VI. *Hume, With Helps to the Study of Berkeley;* VII. *Man's Place in Nature, and Other Anthropological Essays;* VIII. *Discourses, Biological and Geological;* IX. *Evolution and Ethics, and Other Essays*).

Scientific Memoirs. Edited by E. Ray Lankester and Michael Foster. 5 vols. London: Macmillan and Co., 1898–1903.

The Life and Letters of Thomas Henry Huxley. Edited by Leonard Huxley. 2 vols. London: Macmillan and Co., 1900.

Aphorisms and Reflections from the Works of T. H. Huxley. Selected by Henrietta A. Huxley. London: Macmillan and Co., 1907.

Autobiography and Selected Essays. Edited by Ada L. F. Snell. Boston: Houghton, Mifflin Co., 1909.

T. H. Huxley's Diary of the Voyage of H.M.S. Rattlesnake. Edited by Julian Huxley. London: Chatto & Windus, 1935.

Selections from the Essays of T. H. Huxley. Edited by Alburey Castell. New York: Appleton-Century-Crofts, 1948.

Man's Place in Nature. Ann Arbor, Mich.: University of Michigan Press, 1959.

On a Piece of Chalk. Edited and with an introduction by Loren Eiseley. New York: Charles Scribner's Sons, 1967.

2. Uncollected Works

"Scientific Worthies," *Nature,* XVII (March, 28, 1878), 417–20.

Prefatory Note to *Freedom in Science and Teaching* by Ernst Haeckel (New York: Humboldt Library, 1879).

"Reception of the Origin of Species," in *The Life and Letters of Charles Darwin,* ed. Francis Darwin (London: John Murray, 1887), II, 179–204.

"An Apologetic Irenicon," *Fortnightly Review,* LVIII (November, 1892), 557–71.

"Owen's Position in the History of Anatomical Science," in *The Life of Richard Owen* by Richard Startin Owen (London: John Murray, 1894–95), II, 273–332.

"Professor Tyndall," *Nineteenth Century,* XXXV (January, 1894), 1–11.

"Past and Present," *Nature,* LI (November, 1894), 1–3.

"Mr. Balfour's Attack on Agnosticism," *Nineteenth Century,* XXXVII (March, 1895), 527–40.

"Huxley and Agassiz," *Cornhill Magazine,* LV, N.S. (September, 1923), 366–82.

Draft of second part of "Mr. Balfour's Attack on Agnosticism," in *Huxley: Prophet of Science* by Houston Peterson (New York: Longmans, Green and Co., 1932), 315–27.

Selected Bibliography

SECONDARY SOURCES

AINSWORTH DAVIS, J. R. *Thomas H. Huxley*. London: J. M. Dent & Co., 1907. Distinguished chiefly by good explanations of Huxley's work in comparative anatomy and embryology.

ARMSTRONG A. MacC. "Samuel Wilberforce v. T. H. Huxley: A Retrospect," *Quarterly Review*, CCXCVI (1958), 426–37. A discussion of the points at which Darwin's theory conflicts with previously conceived notions of man's origins and the reasons behind Wilberforce's opposition to Darwin.

ASHFORTH, ALBERT. "Spokesman for Darwin and for Science," *New York Times Magazine* (April 7, 1963), 64, 74, 76. Huxley's career and influence analyzed one hundred years after the publication of *Man's Place in Nature*.

AYRES, CLARENCE. *Huxley*. New York: W. W. Norton & Co., Inc., 1932. A good account of Huxley's life.

BIBBY, CYRIL. "Huxley and the Reception of the 'Origin'," *Victorian Studies*, III (1959), 76–86. Full analysis of the sources of opposition to Darwin's theory, and a description of the part played by Huxley in winning acceptance for evolution.

———. "Huxley and University Development," *Victorian Studies* II (1958), 97–116. Assessment of the role played by Huxley—as educator, scientist, and wire-puller—in introducing the study of science and other curriculum reforms to the universities and colleges of nineteenth-century England.

———. "Prince of Controversialists," *Twentieth Century*, CLXI (1957), 268–77. Concise, frequently very amusing account of Huxley's many controversies.

———. *T. H. Huxley, Scientist, Humanist, and Educator*. New York: Horizon Press, 1960. Excellently documented, well-written biography; emphasizes Huxley's work as an educator and administrator.

BLINDERMAN, CHARLES S. "Semantic Aspects of T. H. Huxley's Literary Style," *Journal of Communication*, XII (1962), 171–78. How Huxley employed such rhetorical devices as hyperbole and personification to make difficult material comprehensible to laymen.

———. "T. H. Huxley's Theory of Aesthetics: Unity in Diversity," *Journal of Aesthetics and Art Criticism*, XXI (1962), 49–55. Analysis of Huxley's theories of esthetics; maintains that in his scientific and philosophic work the "architonic faculty was the operative agent."

———. "Thomas Henry Huxley," *Scientific Monthly*, LXXXIV (1957), 171–82. Review of the high points of Huxley's career; description of the qualities which brought him to the fore as a cultural force in nineteenth-century England.

BUCKLER, WILLIAM EARL. "Introduction." *Prose of the Victorian Period.* Boston; Houghton, Mifflin Company, 1958. Revealing discussion of the esthetics of Victorian prose and the relation of Huxley to the other great prose writers of the age.

CLODD, EDWARD. *Thomas Henry Huxley.* New York: Dodd, Mead, & Co., 1902. A conventional Victorian biography written by a friend and admirer of Huxley.

EISEN, SYDNEY. "Huxley and the Positivists," *Victorian Studies,* VII (1964), 337–58. Thorough study of Huxley's controversies with the Positivists, which, according to the author, were instrumental in causing Huxley to "analyze and defend his views on religion and morality."

HOUGHTON, WALTER E. "The Rhetoric of T. H. Huxley," *University of Toronto Quarterly,* XVIII (1949), 159–75. Although he had a reputation for candor and plain speech, Huxley is described as relying heavily on rhetoric for the effectiveness of his writing.

HUXLEY, ALDOUS. "Thomas Huxley as a Literary Man." *The Olive Tree.* London: Chatto & Windus, 1936). Acute analysis of the qualities which give Huxley's writings a permanent place in English letters.

HUXLEY, JULIAN. *Touchstone for Ethics* (contains the 1893 Romanes Lecture of T. H. Huxley and the 1943 Romanes Lecture of Sir Julian Huxley). New York: Harper and Brothers, 1947. Examination of Huxley's reasons for opposing naturalistic theories of ethics in favor of the evolutionary.

IRVINE, WILLIAM. *Apes, Angels, and Victorians.* New York: Meridian Books, Inc., 1959. Classic of Victorian scholarship in which the personal qualities of Darwin and Huxley are compared and contrasted (mostly contrasted) and their respective contributions to the advancement of the evolutionary cause assessed.

———. "Carlyle and T. H. Huxley." *Booker Memorial Studies.* Chapel Hill: University of North Carolina Press, 1950. Carlyle, one of Huxley's first idols, is described as having been a "diminishing force upon his maturer career."

JENSEN, J. VERNON. "The Rhetorical Strategy of Thomas H. Huxley and Robert G. Ingersoll: Agnostics and Roadblock Removers," *Speech Monographs,* XXXII (1965), 59–68. How Huxley and Ingersoll employed such rhetorical devices as irony and ridicule to gain greater freedom for science.

MITCHELL, P. CHALMERS. *Thomas Henry Huxley.* London: G. P. Putnam's Sons, 1900. Engagingly written; sound in its judgments; and, next to Leonard Huxley's, the best of the early biographies on Huxley.

Selected Bibliography

MORE, P. E. "Huxley." *The Drift of Romanticism.* Boston: Houghton, Mifflin Co., 1913. Huxley is described as a frequently superficial, sophistical thinker whose ambiguity of attitude did not suffice to explain "the deeper problems of life."

PATRICK, J. MAX. "The Portrait of Huxley in Mallock's *New Republic,*" *Nineteenth Century Fiction,* XI (1956), 61–69. Mallock's treatment of Huxley is based on a close acquaintance with Huxley's works, but the parody is aimed at particular passages rather than at the basic assumptions of Huxley's thought.

PETERSON, HOUSTON. *Huxley: Prophet of Science.* New York: Longmans Green and Co., 1932. Important biography; contains many valuable insights into Huxley's thought and valuable background material.

STANLEY, OMA. "T. H. Huxley's Treatment of Nature," *Journal of the History of Ideas,* XVIII (1957), 120–27. Suggests that Huxley's originally romantic concept of Nature was substantially altered by reading Mill's essay on "Nature," and that after 1870 his approach to Nature was more scientific.

Supplement to *Nature* CXV (May 9, 1925), 697–752. Recollections of Huxley and an evaluation of his scientific work by a group of English scientists on the one-hundreth anniversary of his birth.

Index

Index